CREATURES OF HABITAT

A 2015 Main Street Rag Anthology

Edited by

Alice Osborn

MINT HILL BOOKS
MAIN STREET RAG PUBLISHING COMPANY
CHARLOTTE, NORTH CAROLINA

Cover art courtesy of Dreamstime, design by M. Scott Douglass

Acknowledgements:

"Son, Your Belongings" by Wanda S. Praisner appeared in *Sensations Magazine Supplement* as well as *Where the Dead Are* (CavanKerry Press, 2013)

"Here After" by Meredith Davies Hadaway is reprinted from *Fishing Secrets of the Dead* (Word Press, 2005)

"The Scow" by Elaine Ford was previously published in *The MacGuffin* and *The American Wife (University of Michigan Press, 2007).*

"Day of the Dead" by Pauletta Hansel was previously published by *Wind*, and also appeared in *First Person* (Dos Madres Press, 2007), *What I Did There: New and Selected Poems* (Dos Madres Press, 2011), *The Lives We Live in Houses* (Wind Publications, 2011)

"The Lord and the Grand Ole Opry" by Gayle Compton previously appeared in *Wind: A Journal of Writing and Community* (Wind, 2002).

"This House" by Lenard D. Moore was previously published in *The Midwest Quarterly*

Library of Congress Control Number: 2015934981

ISBN: 978-1-59948-513-3

Produced in the United States of America

Mint Hill Books
Main Street Rag Publishing Company
PO Box 690100
Charlotte, NC 28227
www.MainStreetRag.com

CONTENTS

INTRODUCTION

Our home can house our greatest triumphs and tragedies. Is buying a home still part of the American Dream—or was it always a fantasy fueled by someone else's desires? Why are so much of our identities tied up to where we live and how big or little our house is? Because these questions nag at me and have become a theme in my previously published work, for this anthology I chose the theme of homes and houses and selected authors who possess a keen eye.

Home is where we love, fight, and endure each other. Where we renovate or tear down—who doesn't wish we could switch out our life as quickly as we can repaint our walls? Our home can be our largest investment and our biggest mistake. Our home can haunt us. Many times what happens inside is vastly different from what the outside world sees. As you will find in the details of these significant stories, poems and essays from these talented authors all across North America, home is one of the most universal elements of storytelling. There's the longing for home from someone who doesn't have one, to the boundaries of protecting one's home and property from outside forces, to the loss and loneliness of leaving our home or having our children leaving us.

Home is also tied to place and community. "Where are you from?" is asked by strangers who want to get acquainted. Usually first memories occur on our stairs, in our basements or bedrooms. Our childhood home may be our safest cocoon or our greatest fear—is it the place we return to or are escaping from in our dreams?

Absorb and connect with these authors and their diverse voices. Welcome the memorable characters and their driveways, gardens, porches, attics and kitchens into your space. After all, home is who we are because everyone has to live somewhere.

Alice Osborn, Editor

WARM

Bob Strother

Lucas Granger pulled the thin cotton blanket tighter around his shoulders and peered over the back seat. The car, a twelve-year-old '70 Dodge sedan, sat nosed-in to a row of bushy, red-berried hollies bordering the Walmart parking lot. He shivered despite the blanket and two layers of clothing covering his skinny body.

For the last three weeks, since they'd been evicted from their rental house, his mom, with Lucas in tow, had applied for work at every business within walking distance of the car—all to no avail. No wonder, he thought. Even at age nine, Lucas knew they looked like what they were—homeless, washing in department store restrooms, sleeping in the car. The little money they'd had was gone within days. Since then, he and his mom made the rounds of the soup kitchens during the day, huddled on benches at the mall between meals, and retreated to the car at night. They'd run the heater off and on until the last of the gasoline played out and the engine coughed, sputtered, and died. That was two days ago.

"It's going to be all right," his mom had told him earlier that evening as he sat with his teeth chattering from the cold. "I'll find a job soon. In the meantime, I'm going to get us another blanket."

"But, Mom—"

She placed a slender finger to his lips. "Don't worry. I'll find a way." Then she left the car, walked the hundred or so yards to the entrance of Walmart, and disappeared inside.

That had been over half an hour ago, and Lucas was worried. He folded the blanket, opened the car door, and stepped out into the parking lot. The wind caused his eyes to tear as he crossed the asphalt, buffeting his small body while he threaded his way among the rows of parked vehicles to the store's entrance. Once inside, he smelled the aromas from the café located to the right of the doorway: frying hamburgers and fresh ground coffee—a beverage he'd never tried but which now seemed very appealing.

Ignoring his rumbling stomach and the saliva building in his mouth, Lucas looked first at the line of checkout stations on his left and then down the long row straight ahead. He opted to walk the aisles from right to left, vowing to search the whole store if he had to. His mom had to be there somewhere. After a while, he found himself in the "Home" section, eyeing the selection of blankets and comforters, noting the prices, and wondering how they could possibly afford one.

It took almost fifteen minutes to search the store, but he saw no sign of his mom. Lucas even checked the restrooms at the rear of the store. He knocked on the ladies' room door and called out softly, "Mom? Are you in there?" Then, a bit louder, "Mom, it's me, Lucas. Are you in there?" When he received no response, he stuffed his hands into his pockets and started back up the long aisle toward the cashiers. Disappointed and a little frightened, he decided to stop at the customer service desk. He'd heard the in-store announcements before, like when a kid got separated from his parents. He'd ask them to page his mom.

He'd covered less than half the distance when he glimpsed a woman who looked like his mom whisked toward the front of the store by a man dressed in blue. It was only for a second, his view cut off by the tall rows of products on either side of the aisle. Still, he recognized the auburn hair and the gray coat. It must be her! "Mom!" he cried. But she was gone. He began to run—twisting and weaving among the shoppers, nearly falling once when he tripped on the wheel of a shopping cart. He slid to a stop at the end of the aisle, his eyes darting in a dozen directions at once. She must be going back to the car. He hurried to the exit just in time to see his mom placed into a police car. No, he thought, this can't be happening.

Lucas pounded on the doors—they were supposed to open automatically—and finally realized he was at the entrance rather than the exit, and lunged to his right. The doors eased open, but too slowly. By the time he squeezed through, the police car was halfway across the parking lot. Lucas raced across the blacktop and almost fell again when a car screeched to a halt just inches from him, its horn blaring. He continued on, half-blind with tears, craning to see over the parked cars and trucks. He saw the police car stop beside the old Dodge, saw the officer get out and look inside, then return to his vehicle and pull away.

Lucas stopped, his breath coming hard, heart fluttering like a caged bird. He stood in the parking lot for what seemed hours but was only minutes, wondering what to do. Somehow, some way, he had to get to his mom. Finally, he returned to the store. In the entranceway, between the two sets of doors, he spotted a wall-mounted pay telephone and, beneath it a ragged copy of the directory. Using his finger to scroll down through the listings, he found the one for the police department. After looking over his shoulder to make sure no one was watching, he tore the page free and stuffed it into his shirt pocket.

Lucas thought about asking one of the shoppers for a quarter so he could call the police, but his mother's words echoed in his mind: We'll never ask for money, Lucas. We're down on our luck, that's all. We may have to eat at the missions, but we're not beggars.

He stepped back inside the store and sat down in the café, his mind a jumble. He waited for over an hour, feeling small and scared and hoping his mother might return. He thought maybe he could ask one of the employees there if he could use their phone. But when he looked, the line of shoppers waiting for customer service stretched almost to the rows of product shelves. Lucas glanced at the clock over the desk—almost closing time. He'd probably never make it. Besides, he'd torn the page out of the telephone directory. They'd see it if he used the phone, and maybe have him arrested, too.

He would spend the night in the car, he thought, just like he'd been doing. And then, in the morning, he'd get directions to the police station, walk all day if he had to, but he'd get there. And he'd be with his mom again.

As soon as he left the store, Lucas saw the flashing lights at the far corner of the parking lot. For a second, he thought the police had returned to take him to his mother. Then he realized the lights were not like the ones he'd seen on police vehicles; they were yellow—the flashing lights of a tow truck—and they were hauling the old Dodge away. He ran once more across the lot, yelling at the top of his lungs for the truck to stop, but the wind swallowed his shouts. The truck turned out of the lot and onto the road. He'd missed it.

What Lucas didn't know—couldn't have known as he stood forlornly in the middle of the parking lot—was that he'd also missed the arrival of a child welfare worker dispatched to collect him. The call went out over the store's public address system moments before closing and seconds after he walked outside: "Lucas Granger, if you are in the store, please come to the customer service desk. We have information about your mother."

Lucas couldn't feel his fingers or his feet. The wind, now full of snow, howled around him, burning his ears and adding to the tears he cried in frustration. He'd walked in what he figured was the general direction of downtown, searching the streaming traffic for a police car. If he could spot one and flag it down, they'd take him to his mother. But the task had proven futile.

After a while, his whole body trembling with cold, he spied a large single-story building set back from the roadside. The sign, mounted on a tall metal pole read "Comfort Inn" and promised single rooms for only fifty-nine-ninety-five a night. With that much money, Lucas thought, we could have bought lots of gas for the car, maybe have gone for weeks running the engine on and off like we did. Oh, how he missed the old Dodge now, his thin cotton blanket, and the smell and feel of his mother's warm body next to his.

Inside the building, behind the big plate glass window, a man sat at a counter, drinking from a white cup. Lucas remembered how the coffee had smelled back at the Walmart, imagined how the liquid would feel warming his belly. He might let me have a cup if I ask nicely. Maybe he would even let me sit for a few minutes in the lobby, just long enough to stop shivering.

Lucas wove his way through a bed of small junipers, stepped out onto the motel's paved parking area, and was heading toward the front door when he noticed a shadowy figure stumble around the far corner of the building. The man had wild eyes and carried something by his side—something that glinted in the light, sharp and dangerous-looking. A knife! Lucas thought.

He ran as fast as he could and spun around the corner of the building farthest from the man, his eyes searching frantically for a place to hide. He spotted a small alcove between the office building and nearest motel room, ducked into the darkened recess, and sat down in the corner, curling his body into a tight ball. It was quiet, protected from the blowing wind and snow. Lucas breathed shallowly, trembling now from fear as well as cold. A few seconds later, a figure appeared at the mouth of the alcove, silhouetted against the wan light creeping in from the parking lot. Lucas drew himself up even tighter, closed his eyes, and waited.

Hoyt Williams chewed and swallowed the last bite of his Cantonese chicken, pushed back from the motel room desk he'd used as a dining table, and carefully folded down the cardboard flaps of the grease-stained take-out containers. The fast food Chinese restaurant wasn't exactly gourmet, but it was cheap and within walking distance. He dropped the remnants of his dinner into the wastebasket and tied the edges of the thin plastic basket liner into a tight knot. Didn't need a smelly reminder of dinner plaguing him through the night; the acid reflux he suffered on the road would be quite enough.

He went into the bathroom, splashed cold water on his face, and thought about calling his wife, but it was already close to eleven, Chicago time. In Atlanta, it was almost midnight. The kids were long asleep, and Dianne wouldn't be happy if the phone woke them on a school night. He sighed. Three client calls in the morning, then a late afternoon flight from O'Hare to Hartsfield International would get him home by nine o'clock if he was lucky. A hurried weekend—soccer and karate with the kids on Saturday, a family dinner and TV that evening—and then back to the grind with a flight out to St. Louis on Sunday afternoon. Not exactly the life he'd dreamed about as a young man, but it paid the bills.

Hoyt removed his shoes, shirt, and trousers and placed them in the closet. He was peeling back the bedcovers when he heard a knock on the motel room door. That's odd, he thought, wondering why anyone would knock at this time of night. He stepped to the door, squinted through the peephole, and saw a man standing on the concrete walkway fronting the row of rooms. Hoyt thought of cracking the door—the chain lock was engaged, and the man didn't immediately appear threatening. But he changed his mind and, instead, pulled aside the drape from the window near the door.

The shaft of light from Hoyt's room bathed the man's grizzled face in a harsh yellow glow. His eyes were red-rimmed, his hair stringy and disheveled, and the wind lashed his tattered coat like the banners flying over Soldier Field. The man held the top of a broken whiskey bottle in his hand, one shard protruding from the bottle's neck like the glistening shaft of a dagger.

"What do you want?" Hoyt shouted through the glass.

The man staggered backward, as if caught off guard by Hoyt's voice, and it was then that Hoyt noticed the stranger's feet were bare. No shoes? It must be fifteen degrees out there!

Then the man lurched toward the window, steadied himself with a hand on the glass, and locked his vacant eyes on Hoyt's. "Do you believe in heaven?" he asked.

Hoyt stared at the man and finally said, "What?"

The man stared back. "Do you believe in heaven?"

Obviously, Hoyt thought, the guy's drunk. He wondered if he should call the motel manager—get the police to come pick him up. But the guy's eyes weren't that of a drunk's. What Hoyt had imagined as alcohol-induced redness now seemed like something far more complicated: lost, soulless, damned. "Sure, I guess so. Why?"

The man nodded, torrents of tears flowing down his stubbly cheeks. "Do you think kids go to heaven? All kids?"

A picture of Hoyt's own children flashed through his brain, snuggled safely in their beds, dreaming maybe. He wanted more than anything else to be home with them, to pull the bedcovers up around their shoulders and give them a goodnight kiss. "Yeah, yeah, I do. I believe all kids go to heaven."

The man nodded again and backed away from Hoyt's window. He turned, stumbled, and caught the portico railing to steady himself. Then he trudged into the parking lot.

Hoyt let the drape slip back into place and stood there for a full minute before sitting down on the side of the bed. He couldn't get those eyes out of his head. And his feet—no shoes in this weather! Pushing himself off the bed, Hoyt went to the suitcase sitting on the foldout luggage rack. He dug around until he found a pair of sneakers—the ones he kept for the rare occasions when he mustered enough energy to use a motel exercise room. He slipped into his slacks and shirt, shrugged into his overcoat, and opened the door to his room. He was probably crazy, but damned if he'd let the guy walk away without something to put on his feet.

Flashing red, white, and blue lights painted the row of motel rooms like a 1970s disco. The patrol car sat in front of the office, exhaust fumes whipping into the air and then disappearing into the maelstrom of driving wind and snow. Hoyt pulled the coat tighter around his neck and made his way toward the lobby. As he passed, he saw the shoeless man in the back of the cruiser. The guy stared straight ahead, like he was somewhere else, his cheeks still glistening with tears.

Inside, the manager leaned on the counter, talking quietly with one of the two police officers. Hoyt waited until they were through and the officer stepped outside to use his radio. "I brought some shoes for that guy. He knocked on my door. I saw he was barefoot."

"Well," the manager said, "yours wasn't the only door he knocked on, and somebody wasn't nearly as compassionate. They called the cops." The manager sidled closer to Hoyt and lowered his voice. "I feel sorry for the poor son of a bitch. Seems his trailer burned to the ground early this morning while he was at work—faulty kerosene heater, or something. Anyway, his two kids were inside. They didn't make it out."

Hoyt thought again about his own kids, thought he'd call his wife after all, regardless of the hour. He set the pair of sneakers on the counter. "See that the cops give him these, will you?"

The manager nodded his agreement, and Hoyt stepped outside into the near blizzard. As he rounded the corner of the lobby, he glanced into the alcove, walked on a few more feet, then paused and came back. He leaned in for a closer look. At first it looked like a pile of rags, but in the scant light, he saw the curvature of a pale forehead. He moved all the way inside and sank to his knees next to the figure. Hoyt brushed a stray lock of hair from the boy's forehead and touched his cheek. It was cold, freezing cold. He felt for a pulse at the boy's throat. Was it there? Did he feel something? He couldn't tell. Hoyt swallowed hard as he hefted the frail bundle and struggled back to the lobby.

The two patrolmen were just getting into their car when Hoyt rounded the corner.

"I need help," Hoyt yelled and pushed through the double entrance doors with the officers trailing behind him.

"What happened?" asked the first officer through the door.

"I don't know. I just found him." Hoyt lowered the boy to a lobby sofa, slipped off his overcoat, and tucked it around the boy's narrow shoulders.

The second officer, the older of the two, frowned. "Is he alive?"

Hoyt knelt and put his hand on the boy's chest. He noted the lack of color in the boy's face and the thin blue lines forming his lips. He looked up at the cop and shook his head. "I don't know."

Lucas kept waiting, expecting at any moment to hear the footsteps of the man who had sent him running for the alcove. But when he dared to open his eyes, the man was gone. After a few minutes, his breathing returned to normal. The wind raged outside his dank refuge, snow swirling like a swarm of mad moths. Lucas tucked his hands under his armpits. He wanted—no, desperately needed—to get up and find his way back to the motel office. But what if the guy's waiting just outside the alcove, ready to grab me? No, it was safer there, in the dark. He closed his eyes again.

At some point, he felt a hand on his forehead—not the gnarled, calloused, claw-like hand he imagined his pursuer would have—but soft, like his mom's. He opened his eyes and she knelt beside him. Mom! I knew you'd come. I knew you'd find me.

It's all right, Lucas. I'm here now. We'll be fine.

She lifted him and nestled him in her arms. Together, they emerged from the alcove and made their way out into the gale. Despite the cold, the wind, and the frenzied snow, Lucas smiled. He looked into his mother's face and saw that she was smiling, too, the kind of smile a mother reserves only for a beloved son.

And, for the first time in what seemed like ages, Lucas was warm.

Bob Strother

PERENNIALS

Mary Elizabeth Pope

Every summer, my husband and I leave behind the academic jobs that keep us in Boston three seasons of the year and trek through western Massachusetts and New York into Canada, crossing into Michigan at Port Huron. By the time we pull up on our lawn in the little town of Northport six hours later and start unpacking, we are bursting with home improvement plans. My husband dreams of adding a deck, an outbuilding that we can use as an office, an actual driveway. I dream of flowers: tulips, hollyhocks, climbing roses, hibiscus. "Our little house in Michigan," we call it. Our little house, we say, in the way that only city-dwellers who have spent a lifetime paying rent can.

But every fall, we close the doors behind us with far fewer of those projects completed than planned. Instead, each year we come away with more proof that while, yes, it is our house, the truth is that it's only ours for a little while. Because what we've discovered in any of the projects we've actually undertaken are the remnants of those dreamed up by previous occupants. In laying the foundation for a patio, we found concrete anchors for a fence that no longer exists;

in pruning a clump of cedars, we ran across a grassed-over sidewalk that connects the front door to the back; in building a stone wall to contain a raised bed for some longed-for hydrangeas, we discovered an enormous decorative pot buried long ago beneath decomposed pine needles until my husband's shovel clinked against the metal rim. He got down on his knees and pried the pot loose, holding it up to me like an archeologist who'd run across an unexpected find.

The house stood empty for twenty years before we bought it, and we're told it belonged to various owners before that, so there's really no one to ask about these discoveries, or about other quirks that suggest the house's changing of hands: a second chimney that has no corresponding fireplace; floorboards that run perpendicular to one another from room to room; an entryway that has two log-cabin walls that match nothing else about the house. Those walls were painted mustard yellow when we bought it, though sometimes a chip pries loose to reveal that beneath the old yellow paint was green, and beneath the green, red. Once, I even found a strand of hair frozen in the yellow I was endeavoring to cover with white. I stood there for a long time, realizing someone just like me had stood there years before, with hair as long as mine, a paintbrush in her hand.

My favorite discovery, however, is one we made our very first year—day lilies planted in inexplicable locations around our small yard. When they first began to bloom, I thought of them as obstacles to my sweeping plans to turn the lawn into something I'd seen in *Better Homes and Gardens*. But now when they show their faces each July, I find that instead of thinking them a bother, I'm grateful to the person who planted them. Besides that raised hydrangea bed and a few stems of clematis I've managed to plant, we've never gotten around to landscaping the yard the way we'd hoped, and I'm starting to doubt we ever will. Instead, I understand that perhaps more than anything, our best offerings to the house are those we will pass on one day, giving solace to its future owners for all their own unfinished plans.

Lenard D. Moore

THIS HOUSE

So this is how I enter:
I walk the AstroTurf that stretches
down the walkaway my brother laid after shop class.
The leafing maple in the afternoon breeze
shakes over a twisted hump of roots
like loosened braids of brown rope.
The wooden steps have been reduced to stone.
When I was too little to climb them,

and got wet paint on my green jackets,
my mother's hand thrashed my behind.
I open the windowless door so slowly.
My father and mother look up at me,
lowering the newspapers on their laps.
I enter my old bedroom
where every morning the bird song
with its familiar cadence woke me,

where posters of my father and mother that I thumb-tacked
to the wall two decades ago still hang.
Their round, unlined faces remind me
that I will grow old like them,
like this house heated by the sun,
dustless as a new coffin.
When I turn around,
their living faces look back at me

like tattered posters.
How sunlight slips between us,
seems white through white lulling curtains,

and hums throughout this house.
We settle in the living room,
our eyes shiny as polished pennies.
This house gives us plenty to talk about,
years emptying through the same door.

Lenard D. Moore

Beth Copeland

SELF-PORTRAIT AS A HOUSE

In kindergarten I drew a picture of a house—
one red square with two square windows like eyes
on either side of a brown door without a knob,
each window divided into four square panes,
topped by a triangular roof like a folded newspaper hat,
a black coil of smoke rising from the stovepipe chimney,
and my name printed at the bottom in block letters
anchoring my house to earth—BETH,
meaning house in Hebrew,

which may explain why I collect miniature houses
and line them up on shelves like Shinto shrines,
and why there are houses embroidered on guest towels
and a row of houses on the wallpaper border in my bathroom,
and why a house was the one thing I wanted when I grew up—
not a diamond ring, or car, or Imelda Marcos collection
of spike-heeled designer shoes—just a house,
a symbolic extension of the self,
a container for all the rooms of my life,

beginning with the prefabricated house in Fukuoka.
One night the roof blew off during a typhoon.
After that, we moved to a house where Japanese
children pressed their noses against the windows,
peering in at my sisters and me
when we had to take naps after lunch.
We hated going to sleep, so we'd jump
on our beds and pretend to be Sumo wrestlers
by wedging our underpants up our butt cracks.

I don't remember the house in Louisville
where we lived when I was three, but I recall the Campbell's
Kids
on a soup label and eating Frosted Flakes and watching
Howdy Doody
on TV and taking a bath with a Clarabell the Clown
washrag and the pink-eyed rabbit at the nursery school
where my best friend was a girl named Jeannie
and my boyfriend was a Chinese kid who accidentally
hit me in the head with a brick.
I had to have three stitches.

After we moved back to the house in Fukuoka,
I learned to print my name in English
and practiced writing
Japanese
characters
in
a
vertical
line.

When we moved to Wake Forest we lived
in a big white house with a wrap-around porch.
Once, some girls came over for a slumber party,
and everyone was scared when they heard my father
snoring downstairs, thinking it was Bluebeard's ghost.
I shone a flashlight on the ceiling,
slowly bringing a giant shadow hand down
to grab them. I wrote my name
on the wall inside my closet before we left

for Benares, where we lived in a bungalow
where geckos clung to the walls with tiny suction-cup feet,
and a rat we nicknamed Riki Tiki Tavi
squeezed through drainage holes to my sister's bedroom at night.

There were no screens on the windows to keep out mosquitos
 and flies,
no hot water, no refrigerator or oven, only a charcoal stove
where Abdul prepared our meals of water
buffalo and mashed potatoes molded
into swans with carrot slice beaks,

until we returned to the house in Wake Forest,
where my name was still written on the closet wall,
but the other eighth-grade girls thought I was weird
because I'd never heard of the Beatles and used the word
 "queer"
to refer to anything odd or unusual, and when the boy sitting
 behind me
said, "Eat me...eat me raw," I said, "Why would I want
 to do that?"
thinking he was talking about some "queer" form
 of cannibalism
practiced in redneck regions of the Appalachians,
which only encouraged him to keep pestering me

until we moved to the brick split-level house in Raleigh.
I had a basement room with a twin bed and small maple desk
where I wrote poetry late at night instead of studying
for chemistry tests, secretly wishing my name
was melodious like Amelia Rose or Meredith
or French like Solange or Yvette, instead of
Beth, a one-syllable name that can be uttered
in a single breath. Beth, as stolid and plain
as the four-square house with forest green shutters

where I lived when my children were young,
after a decade of dorm rooms and apartments before
 I was married.
Once, a drunk man at a bar said, "Baby, you're built like a brick
shit house," a backhanded compliment, I guess,
since to be a house, even an outhouse,

is to be grounded, rooted to earth,
and I was ready to settle down and stay in one place
instead of traveling with only the contents of a suitcase
and a map I never figured out how to read,

even when I held it sideways to read the names
of North-South streets that, like Japanese, are written vertically
instead of left to right or West to East.
The house in Chicago was on a one-way street
which made it hard to give directions to anyone
who visited, but it had an old oak staircase I stripped
to a Norwegian blonde sheen and an enclosed porch
painted white,
with wicker chairs and plantation blinds that reminded me
of the house in Wake Forest that I love best

of all the houses I've lived in and left.
Now I live in a blue house without geckos, rats or ghosts,
in a sleepy suburb where neighbors drive into attached garages
and are never seen. This may be the last house I'll inhabit
on Earth,
except for the house of flesh and bone I was given at birth,
along with my name, Beth.

A name that can be uttered in a single breath.
In this house with charcoal-gray shutters.
In this house that rhymes with death.

Beth Copeland

A HOUSE IS NOT A HOME

Arthur Carey

The clock on the mantle chimed as the hands registered 6 a.m. On the floor, sleeping on a blanket by the fireplace, the golden lab raised its head and snuffled.

Janie stirred on the couch and opened her eyes. "Shush, Rufus."

She swung her feet to the floor and yawned. This was her last night tossing on the bumpy leather couch. All couches are uncomfortable for sleeping overnight, she decided. Too soft, too hard, too something or other. But this wasn't her couch or her house or her home. And Rufus wasn't her dog. Janie was homeless, and this house-and pet-sitting gig was ending. Where would she sleep tonight? Too early to worry about that.

She pawed through her backpack and donned a T-shirt, jeans and sweater. Then she slipped into the guest bath and scrubbed up, taking care to wipe off the sink. After running a comb through short, brown hair, she examined herself in the mirror. Puffy, tired green eyes stared back through round glasses with plastic frames. Light glinted off a small piece of tape on a hinge.

Still yawning, she walked into the kitchen, dog at her heel, and opened the refrigerator. She drained the O.J.

container she'd brought and popped the last two slices of bread in the toaster.

The dog waited patiently as she refilled its water dish, ladled out some dry food into a bowl, and carried the dishes out to the patio. "Come on, Ruf."

Janie scooped up the blankets on the couch and returned them, neatly folded, to the closet in the master bedroom. She never slept in the beds. Too personal. She pulled out her cell phone to check the bus schedule. She suspected most of her friends regarded a cell phone as a convenience, not a necessity. But to her a cell phone was a survival tool. She ordered her life with it. Minutes later, bus pass in hand, Janie was out the door. She hid the house key in a flowerpot overflowing with red geraniums.

Students crowded the entrance to John C. Fremont High School when she arrived. Janie hurried to her homeroom, so she could begin lining up a place to crash that night. She ran the morning's schedule through her mind: English at 8:15 a.m. She'd be late with a paper on George Orwell's *Animal Farm*, but at least she'd finished the reading after work at Boony Burgers. Then came gym at 9:15, chemistry at 10:15, and history, her favorite class, at 11:15.

Lunchtime arrived. Students jammed the cafeteria. Janie got milk and a salad and spied her friend Jake. She plunked down in a chair he'd piled with books to save for her.

She had a long history with Jake, stretching back to when they'd giggled over dissecting worms in freshman biology class. She attended concerts to hear him play trumpet in the school band and considered him her only male friend. She had no time in her life for guys.

"Want some of my fries?" Jake tempted her with a limp potato slice dangled in the air.

"Yuck!" Janie recoiled. "I smell that stuff three hours a day, five days a week at work. I can't get the odor of grease out of my hair."

She looked at him suspiciously and leaned forward. "Can you smell anything?"

"No." He flushed.

"Honest?"

"Well…Maybe a little," he said. The words came out slowly as he debated how to avoid hurting her feelings.

"Curse of the fry babies," Janie sighed.

"Fry babies?"

"That's what kids who work fast food get called behind their backs."

"That's hardcore!" he said, shaking his head.

"The gunk settles into the fibers of our uniforms and then into the skin itself," Janie continued. "It's like an invasion by microscopic aliens, and you can smell it sometimes." She shrugged. "People look at you differently if you stick out. Like there's a club and you don't belong. They don't intend to be mean."

Jake slathered another fry with ketchup and dowsed it with salt.

"What's with you?" Janie asked.

"The usual. I aced my biology test and got a D in trigonometry."

"Trig's tough," she agreed.

"Spring band concert's this Saturday," he said, perking up. "Seniors get solos. Bring your parents."

"Can't." Janie took a sip of milk. "Out of town. I told you that."

"That's what you always say. You…"

"Stop fishing!" Her eyes flashed a warning.

"I'll tell you what the deal is, but if you breathe a word I'll take that horn and put a dent in your skull."

"Okay…Okay…" he replied.

"My mom lost her job and moved to Nevada to look for another one," she said in a low voice. "She changed her cell number and she doesn't call. Then the rent ran out. I had to move out."

"Wow!" Jake gave a low whistle. "Where are you staying?"

"Around." Janie didn't tell him that "around" meant often not knowing where she was going to sleep at night. Uncertainty had become a constant in her life. She'd started chewing her fingernails from the stress.

"Bummer … Man, that's a bummer," he said.

"It is what it is." She liked that phrase. It summed up recognition of life's unfairness without excuse or apology.

"How do you get away with it? Doesn't the school send mail home?"

"I cut a deal with the woman who moved into our old apartment. I baby-sit for her once a month. She holds the mail for my mom. I answer it when I have to. Most of it is junk you can toss."

"You sign report cards, too?"

"Why not?" she said. "I get good grades. Besides, who's to know?"

"You rock, J!" He gave her an admiring nod.

She pointed a threatening finger at him. "Not a word to anyone or they'll dump me in foster care. I'd lose my job and my freedom! After graduation no one will be checking up on me."

A bell rang and students began leaving the cafeteria.

Janie whipped out her datebook between math class and study hall to check the friends who let her sleep over. She rotated names on the list. Going to a shelter wasn't an option. She'd stayed in one once, but the snoring and smell got to her and people asked too many questions.

She spent most evenings at the public library, which didn't close until 9, or at the home of a friend. She had scored a few nights lately with Mary Buschetti, her best friend. But Mr. Buschetti had frowned when she explained—again—that her mother was out of town and she was afraid to sleep alone in the apartment. Even the best excuses wear thin over time.

"Yo! Janie!" A familiar male voice rose over the chatter of students passing to class.

She turned to see Andy Nguyen.

"My star reporter! What have you got for me? The giant presses are waiting!"

She shook her head. Nguyen loved his role as editor of the school newspaper, "*The Talisman*," and called everyone on the staff a "star reporter."

"Just an early piece on the prom, Andy," she said. "I talked to Mrs. Yarosky, the adviser. She hinted the chaperones would be coming down hard on drinking this year."

"Party on for me." He grinned. "We lowly juniors have to wait a year."

"No prom for me." She shook her head. "My parents are dragging me out of town to a family reunion."

"Whoa, that's a downer," he said. "Hey, gotta bounce. See you in J-lab tomorrow."

Janie looked away. A boy in her history class had invited her to the prom, but she had turned down the invitation with the same lie. She suspected Jake would have asked her, but she had made it clear she wouldn't be going. Proms were a big deal—a big expensive deal. They required a fancy dress, shoes, hair styling and parties. No money for that. It would have been nice to go to the prom. She had helped decorate the one the year before that transformed the gym into a Parisian nightclub. The prom was another piece of life missed.

Classes ended and Janie checked her cell phone while waiting for a bus to take her to work. There were no messages for Homebodies, Inc. She double-checked the Internet blurb promoting her house sitting service: *Leaving town? Need someone to water the plants, feed the cat and keep the lights on at night? Homebodies, Inc., will do it all at reasonable rates. References available.* Most of her jobs house sitting came from the ad and word of mouth.

Where could she crash tonight? With Melanie? She hadn't leaned on her for a while. No. Melanie's brother was staying over. Rosa? Rosa might work, but she'd been there three weeks ago. Karla! She'd call Karla! Karla was overweight, lacked a boyfriend, and had her own apartment. When Janie stayed with her, she brought leftover food from Boony Burgers. Karla got off on Boony Biggies. Janie's fingers flicked over the screen.

The day shift manager, Mr. Sampson, waved Janie over as soon as she arrived at Boony Burgers. "Miguel is late again," he fussed. "Also, Irma has a bad cold and was sneezing. I sent her home."

She waited.

"Grab a headset and handle the drive-thru orders. You'll have to work the fry station, too, until Miguel comes in. After that you can cover the front counter."

"I worked fries yesterday, Mr. Sampson," Janie said. "I was hoping to work the dressing station." She liked the dressing station. The routine of putting lettuce, tomatoes, onions and cheese on hamburgers, wrapping them in paper, and putting them in boxes let her mind ramble. Also, she got to chat with other workers and learn some Spanglish.

"I'll spell you as soon as I can," the manager promised.

Janie's shoulders slumped. At least she kept busy working the drive-thru window. The orders flowed into her headset, a stream of slurred, garbled speech in the vocabulary of fast food: *Boony'sBiggiewithfries…CokeandBoonychicken bitsfortwo,smallsalad…BabyBoonywithtoy, DoubleBoonyyandbiggiefriesandachocolatecookie… Plainhamburgernodressing,CalorieCutterside…"*

By 7 p.m., she was pooped. After work, Ramon, who had worked the fry station, gave her a ride to Karla's. She spent three nights with Karla, until she sensed Karla was losing her appetite for burgers and fries. She finished the paper on "Animal Farm." Then she got lucky. A man and wife hired her to house sit for a week while they visited relatives on the East Coast. Yes! That meant kitchen privileges and lengthy showers, unlike the quickies after gym class.

Time compressed: school, work, sleep. Only one issue of The Talisman remained. Andy Nguyen prowled the front of the journalism lab wearing his serious editor's expression. "We need to do something hard hitting for the last issue, something memorable," he said. "Ideas?"

They came quickly: Student drinking...Buying essays online...Lying on college applications.

"Been there, done that last year," Nguyen said.

"Why not interview that freshman kid who dozes through study hall every third period? I hear he sleeps in a shelter," said Maria Gomez. "And there are a couple of kids who come to school in cars piled high with clothes and stuff. Looks like they're living in them."

"I know the kid in study hall." Alicia Palmer rolled her eyes. "He looks like a train wreck. Clothes rumpled, hair uncombed. I sit way, way back from him."

Janie fumed. Alicia was blonde, wore her cheerleader's sweater in warm weather and yawned frequently. She rarely wrote anything for the school paper and when she did, it usually required heavy editing. She didn't know a comma from an apostrophe and didn't care.

"Are there other homeless kids in class?" Nguyen asked.

Janie zoned out. She could give them the real scoop on what it was like to be homeless, to scramble for a place to sleep every night, to wear the same clothes. And in her case, to fly solo. But she wouldn't. No way she'd let stuck-up kids like Alicia Palmer look down on her. Worse, the administration would know she'd been signing her mother's name to stuff. Goodbye honor roll, goodbye college recommendations, goodbye chances of a scholarship. Hello, strangers running her life.

"I like it...I like it," Nguyen said. He roamed the front of the classroom, hands spread as if embracing a new and unexpected vision. "I see poverty vs. plenty; sacrifice vs. entitlement; struggles in a grim, heartless society vs. the comfy cocoon of the classroom."

"Bor…ing," Alicia Palmer said. "So there are a few homeless kids. Big deal."

"Some? There are hundreds of thousands out there," Janie said. "They struggle to get through each day. It's a national problem."

"I didn't mean…" Alicia began, shoulders stiffening.

"Whoa!" The editor stepped in, cutting her off. "I like what I'm hearing. This is a social issue with an edge…and right here."

"Hundreds of thousands?" He looked at Janie, who nodded.

"I did a report for social studies."

"Okay, gang," Nguyen said, slapping a desk for emphasis. "We've got a hot possibility. But first we've got to find some homeless students. Then we'll put together a story and drop a bomb on old John C. Fre." He turned to Janie. "Since you did a report, you know where to dig for background. Find me some stats, numbers…costs… anecdotes." He paused. "You can write the story."

My bad. Now what? Janie groaned to herself.

She turned to the Internet. She found The U.S. Department of Education estimated there were one million homeless students in the United States. *One million!*

The Talisman ran a small story on the front page of the next-to-last issue asking homeless students to contact the paper. A reporter for a daily newspaper noticed it and contacted the principal for information. Andy Nguyen was summoned to the principal's office.

He wants us to kill the story," Nguyen said at a hastily called meeting of *The Talisman* staff. "He says it would leave a bad impression about the school."

"You mean because he didn't even know how many homeless students go to John C. Fre?" a student laughed.

"That, too." Nguyen shrugged. "Plus our advisor, Miss Sloan, asked me to reconsider doing the story."

Silence.

Janie waited for Nguyen to defend running the story despite what the principal and advisor wanted. He didn't.

"What if we didn't do a news story?" asked Maria Gomez, who had come up with the idea in the first place. "What if somebody wrote an opinion piece? Same effect. The problem gets aired."

More silence.

"Yeah, but who'll write it?" Nguyen said.

"Janie's done the research," Alicia Palmer said. She toyed with a curl and smiled.

The next day, Janie sat in front of one of the Journalism lab's two aging Apple computers, ignoring the blinking cursor. She had slept little, agonizing over what to say... and what the effect could be on her personally. Why not just dump the assignment? Let someone else do it. But there was no one else. She stared at the computer screen. And then she began typing.

They sit next to us at assemblies, hurry down the hallways between classes, and try to keep their lives a secret. But if you look closely, sometimes their clothes don't match or aren't pressed. Sleeping in a car does that. Sometimes they may not smell good because washing up at a service station where you have to get a key to use the restroom isn't easy.

Worse, unthinking students sometimes snicker at them for dozing off in class, unaware that living in a motel or being shuffled between relatives affects you physically as well as mentally.

Who are the kids we ignore? They are John C. Fremont's homeless students. I know because I'm one of them.

BEING A HOME

J. D. Cortese

The house has a strange feeling about it, as if in a year it forgot being ours. Even the night seems darker from inside, and the spotlights that peer at our walls have been weakened by the wait. A year abroad and what was once home now looks only like a place. Not as impersonal as a hotel but halfway to becoming one.

The reasons for my leaving were not as clear as the pressures that have taken me back, closer to my old planet. We might have been offered jobs, and felt the renewed call of our supposed vocations, but what eventually lifted us from the familiar surfaces of other countries was more the product of randomness than planning. The house wouldn't understand that, an animal that knew of our presence only as warm shadows moving within its entrails.

As I stumble into a walk-in closet, still mercifully illuminated, the smell of hanged clothes hits me with a mix of acidity and dampness. It has been a while since I wore those suits and the academic robe; the tie rack is in need of batteries. I have grown out of my professorial formalities and no longer recognize my old self, the one the house might remember, always on the way to meetings and lecture rooms. It's a different me that ambles around in microfiber shirts and rugged jeans, adapted for a life in the tropics.

Feeling a little anxious, I turn all the lights on and two of them don't work. The fridge smells of leftover food from the occasional stays of my son and the bathtub has had visits from a colony of ants that climbed its thirsty pipes. Our cat's untimely death—half a world away to witness it—remains in the great beyond of ammoniac smells that percolate the atomic structure of our carpets. And my books have been sleeping unopened, tucked in by the pressing proximity of their neighbors.

Everything we had seems to have been replaced by a precise copy, but I don't feel any empathy for these new versions. I'm beginning to understand how our lives are sustained by the memories we make every day, but since there's only so much of them that can be held on the fickle memory of objects, they can be replaced by newer ones. Or by their absence. If we aren't around to create our own spaces of memory in the world, what's left behind slowly vanishes.

My house was once a neat compartment of the world we created to reflect our selves, but now only remains as an extension of the same world. A world that's fleeting, full of rules, and not in any need of our permanent advice and presence. Not unlike an airport, but one of immense size and thus able to host all of our lives, as we eat in restaurants, shop in lighted galleries, and sleep in private quarters if we have high enough status. And we do have that on the country I'd reached for outside of my own origins, the right of having big houses and not being wretched by viruses, parasites, or explosions. We are passengers of first class here, and the world is just a hotel we inhabit until we depart for other, so far undiscovered destinations. I have made the mistake of believing our house, my home, was not a part of that undetermined, dangerous world.

My queasy stomach tells me that I'm learning a harsh lesson, one I didn't want to get and especially not from one of my own. The passing of time, which should have made our house into more of a home than before, has unmade it into a stranger. Yes, I could tell her that I am here; that those thousands of books burdening the foundation are all mine; that all these smells coming from whatever is left from the paints we'd used to recolor the rooms are my doing; that we lived here and she cannot forget us so soon. But this won't change her back to what she was.

The house is now proof that the hands of time don't built or give, just take away. Time passes and erases it all, even us, but it first blurs the fingerprints of our lives. No matter the pressure we have applied to make our imprint, time would make it fade away every second of every minute, and at the end, like an incomplete slice of the moon, melt with everything else into the night unremembered. We are all the time going into that quiescent night, and what we have, or believe we have, is as transient as our efforts.

I turn some switches on and then off. Wash some clothing and my bed linens to make noise, and thaw in the microwave a friend's misplaced lasagna. For some good measure, I separate in piles the contents of my luggage. It's late enough to be just about the house and me, and I don't want to lie in the dark with her. And so I walk upstairs a couple more times, reassuring myself that the only monsters I could find are the product of my own evanescence, the unassailable evidence that I am made of even less durable materials that everything else around me.

Finally, on my way to the kitchen, I pass near the garden windows and the house wakes up—my motion being recognized and greeted with light rather than by a swinging tail. We are in the middle of the night and the house has remembered me. We are starting to be friends again.

I pick up my favorite air freshener and start to walk around, mindlessly spreading the lavender smell of our first apartment in Buenos Aires, of the Fulton cologne my mother once gave me as a birthday gift, and of the other many places where I have been present and felt to be mine. The molecules move and connect with the house's atoms in the wall of our cave, and the night of forgetfulness starts to recede again.

At least for the time being. And only if I stay here.

Rafael Jesús González

HOME BUILDING

I

The round window
    cut
has captured a star
    smack damn at center—
the roof beams
hold up the sky—
    they are red
as the cliffs of Chaco—
naked as they are
they seem as precarious.
    What isn't?
The holes we open
in our lives
can be pitfalls—
    or they can close
shutting us in darkness—
the rooms fall.
The ancients shored
their crumbling cliffs;
    they put turquoise
    in the cracks
    to appease the gods.
Before going off to work
I make my offering:
    in the tool box,
nestled among hammers & chisels,
a rose.

Rafael Jesús González

II

The spaces finished,
windows open to new seasons—
the past ones,
now inviolable,
rest in the gods' hands.
The offerings have been made:
Last year's roses
turquoise & mother-of-pearl
jade & unrepeatable words
encased within the walls
where ancient kings would lay
the body of the architect
killed to guard the secret
& appease the gods.
(We do the tea ceremony
& what blood there is
stays in the heart.)

WHERE THE HEART IS

Jane Andrews

If my brother dies, and I can only write this because it seems he might not after all; if he dies, it is not just Frank who is gone. If he dies, our parents die again. His memories of them and the memories he shares with me of them will be gone. Totally gone. If he dies, our second mother, Nolie and our grandmother and our Aunt Teeny all but disappear. Uncle Buster, too. Mrs. McCann, the Dillards, the older Frank and I get, the older everyone gets, the fewer witnesses are left who recall these people. Especially our mother and father. And if Frank goes, he takes them with him.

If he were a house, he'd be condemned. We are lucky the surgeons were able to go in and repair and renovate instead of just letting him fall apart. In real estate jargon, I guess he's been flipped. Maybe I'll start calling him "Flipper." Frank is in a cardiac ICU thousands of miles away in Oregon recovering from a heart valve replacement and a double heart bypass. I'm given phone and email updates on my brother by his wife, Wendy. We've all been through this before, as this is Frank's second valve replacement; his first was when he was thirty-nine. He is fifty-five now.

The bypasses are new, and there seems to be significant leakage. The "root" is compromised. Degraded. Something like a frayed piece of cloth that makes for an insecure seam. Wendy tells me that when he came out of anesthesia, from a three or four hour operation that took six or seven hours, he gave her a wink. *I'm awake, I'm alert, I love you*. That's their signal. Frank is the genetic heir of heart trouble, our father having died from the same thing at forty, and his father at forty-three. The joke at reunion picnics: *Q: What do you call a man over fifty in our family? A: Adopted.*

The evening before he had surgery my brother called me "just in case." We talk several times a week anyway, even when he is travelling for work as a corporate speaker and stand-up comedian. "I'm sorry I stole your knitting needles and charged you five dollars to find them," he said. "I'm sorry I made you drink shoe polish." I told him it's okay. I reminded him that when asked what I wanted to be when I grew up, my answer was "Frank." He is the man I measure other men by, personally and professionally. I have never known anyone with a more loving nature or natural integrity. "I'm sorry I caught you in the burglar trap and you had to get a tetanus shot," I told him. Once I set out a wooden board with rusty five inch nails standing up to catch potential felons. Frank stepped on it barefoot driving his whole weight down on a nail and skewering his arch. It must have hurt like an SOB. Tetanus shots hurt, too. "That's okay, Jane Bloss," Frank said, using my parents' nickname for me. He is the only one I allow to use it. You don't want just anybody calling you "Blossom." I said, "Thanks, Bootie. I love you. You are the best brother." We always say *I love you* before hanging up the phone. Because you never know. It could be the last time. You never know.

And here we are, Frank and Wendy and me and all the other people who love Frank, not knowing. Everyone loves Frank, but I have loved him the longest. As he has loved me. Frank was three and a half years old when I was born, so he remembers a life before me. But I have never lived without the surety of his presence. We are the single survivors of our family, of our history. I feel things that I don't even have words for. I don't even know if such words exist. I feel the usual things of course, fear, anxiety, hope, helplessness. But there's more. A taut vibration in my body that must make a sound only dogs can hear. A primal panic that has settled in my lungs like a heavy dark gas. A wonderment that I can and must continue to do all the daily things. A searingly urgent need to talk to someone who gets it. Who knows that to lose Frank, for me, would be more than sad. Because he contains more. It would be like a star collapsing into itself. A gravity that hardly allows light to escape. If you don't know what I mean or you think I am exaggerating, then God bless you, I hope you never do know. But if you do, and you ever need someone to listen, I'm your gal.

One of the daily things I had to do was give my twenty-three-year-old daughter Phoebe a ride to the family doctor for a check-up. Dr. Marucheck was Frank's primary physician when Frank lived in Raleigh years ago. People in the office remember him and always ask about him. I told them about his surgery and they expressed concern.

On the way back from Marucheck's office in North Raleigh with Phoebe, I impulsively took a sharp right turn off Anderson Drive onto Drewry Lane. It was out of our way and I had not been down that road for several years. It is the street Frank and I grew up on. I wanted to see our mother Dixie's house. Dixie died in 1987 and the house has been sold a couple of times since. Maybe I thought if I could feel a connection to the house I wouldn't feel so far away from my brother.

The mimosa tree that was home base for kickball was long gone, of course. The new owners had added a cement parking pad and turned the carport into a garage. The house itself was remodeled beyond recognition. Actually, it was prettier, with a little porch and bumped out windows. The backyard was still fenced in, so I thought they might have dogs. I parked the truck on the street in front of the house next door. Bunnie Browning's house while we lived in the neighborhood.

"I'm going to check out the backyard," I told Phoebe, unbuckling my seat belt.

She looked alarmed.

"No, you are *not*," she hissed.

I think she was afraid I'd set off a security alarm and get arrested for trespassing. It's the kind of thing I would do, accidentally. They did have an ADT sign in the front yard.

"Yes, I am," I said, sliding out of the truck. "You don't know me."

"You got that right," Phoebe said, slumping in her seat and turning her attention to her smart phone.

It was four o'clock in the afternoon and there were no cars parked in either driveway. I walked like an Egyptian, sliding sideways between the Browning's house and camellias that grew two feet taller than my head. I peeked a diagonal look at my old backyard. A weird skinny cement patio ran from the back door where Frank once put his hand through the glass, to the end of the house where his room used to be. Beyond that was grass. Just grass and what looked like a smaller fenced in area for a dog that either wasn't there or didn't notice me. Grass. The retaining wall and steps gone. There was still a picture window running the length of the living room to give a view to the backyard. Frank and Dixie and I could gaze out on a late spring day and see red and white azaleas exploding on either side of three brick steps. Purple vinca with star-shaped blooms and glossy leaves at the top of the retaining wall, and tiger lilies, daffodils, forsythia, quince, roses, bridal veil, camellias of different varieties, and things I never knew the name of.

Above all this was the three story tree house with a ladder and a medicine cabinet Frank and his friend Johnny Dillard (a boy who started collecting potential serial killer merit badges early) built to house the Rat Fink Club. To join the Rat Fink Club, a kid had to jump three stories down without using the ladder. Except for me, because it was my yard and I was the youngest. Also, I think Frank knew that if he let me jump and I got hurt, he would be in big trouble. Then, our backyard had gone on forever. At least to a red clay bank where we dug foxholes and watched the cars on Six Forks Road. The lower portion of the yard with grass and a rotating clothes line, plus a brick patio were also gone.

Looking at the now smooth expanse of fescue, I wondered if when tearing out all the flowers and bushes and trees, the new owners discovered the little rise where we buried our pets. Every turtle, fish, hamster, rabbit, lizard, mouse, and cat. All those funerals Nolie performed. All those bones. What must the new owners have thought about us, the people who lived there before. What kind of strange voodoo did they attribute to us? Probably, they also found the last of my mother's Reed & Barton sterling silver flatware which we used to dig in the yard and forgot. Looking over the fence into 215 East Drewry Lane, there was nothing for me to see. There was nothing of all our history left to show we ever lived there. I hope the next owners have kids and flowers and a tree house. And pets.

I sighed and squeezed along the fence toward the street. When I got to the truck, Phoebe looked up.

"You took a picture with your phone, didn't you?"

"No," I said, "There's nothing to take a picture of."

I looked across the street.

"You see that house there..." I began, and gave Phoebe a guided tour of the houses and families and events of my childhood on that street until we reached what was called "the circle" and said, "This is where we played dodge ball and I still have a scar on my right knee." Then I turned the truck back to a main road and headed home.

I guess I wanted Phoebe to know my childhood with me, including her Uncle Frank and her grandparents who died before she was born. Phoebe has a brother, too, my son Duncan. She doesn't quite get what I feel as I wait for Frank to get better or worse, to live or to die, to want to know and to fear knowing. But she's a sensitive person with more than her share of empathy. So she listened to me, understanding that I needed to tell her things.

"Why didn't you and Dad live in that house after you got married?" she asked me.

"Too many ghosts," I said, shrugging. "But now, I kind of welcome ghosts. I just don't want my brother to be one any time soon."

"I thought you didn't believe in ghosts," Phoebe said, looking at me.

I looked back her. "I don't. Unless I need to," I said.

Now I'm at home, waiting on a phone call, hoping I don't need to.

Dawn Leas

CARPET CLEANING

After the house empties
and the leaves begin their turning,
we assess years of living. Children
with cleats. Pets and juice spills. Walls

adorned with scuff marks and nail pops.
Faded front door, uneven sidewalks,
so many *I'll-get-to-it-next-weekend* chores.
In the family room, we map the revolving

seasons in the carpet, a connect-the-dots of our life.
Can it be saved? you ask.
For a few minutes, I study the mosaic of dirt,
stains and spot-treated circles.

Sure, I shrug, *anything can be saved.*
The question is...how badly do you want it?

Jackie Craven

STOPPING BY MY CHILDHOOD HOME

After hours of driving, I find it at the bottom
of a cul-de-sac—a modernist house,
all glass and steel and trapezoids,
bright as a chip of ice.

I idle at the curb and swear I hear
cocktail laughter jingle above the zigzag roof.
I'm a child again, watching my parents
glide up and down Escher stairs.

Their festive guests shimmer
through transparent doors,
flooding turquoise rooms with frozen light
like fossil fireflies.

The remembered scent of smoke and olives
drifts across the empty patio.
Ice cubes ping, glasses chime,
amber voices call me in.

Wanda Praisner

SON, YOUR BELONGINGS

Space now for visiting grandchildren,
told of your one-dimpled smile,
thumbs and knees that bent backwards.

A room you expected to return to
emptied: furniture, books, clothes—
a room it took years for us to enter.

One last pile remains centered
on the new carpet—the momentum lost:
a plastic Sheraton ice bucket you took
because the "S" stood for your name;

your Polaroid, strap broken;
a pair of Nike's, split at the soles;
college notebooks—
the last date: September 15, 1986.

What your brothers call "trash,"
what they don't want, I return
white-boxed like a casket to your closet—
even the sneakers, still laced.

AMONGST OTHER THINGS

Tom Quinn

Of all the things in the garage to go after, she went for the golf clubs first, untangled them from a string of extension cords and wrestled them onto the driveway. Next was the snow blower, and then the tractor, right out alongside with the golf clubs. That was the sell pile. Her husband walked right past her to the end of the driveway where he lit up a cigarette and drew on the tobacco as if he were trying to pull himself through the filter to a different time and place.

The sun was well up. And the dew on the grass sparkled. The cigarette was terrific, nothing to deny him the pleasure of a nice, quiet smoke until he heard her voice from the garage. He dug his teeth into the cigarette, one last drag before flipping it onto the street. When he turned, he saw beach chairs and umbrellas and other things loaded one on top of the other. She came from the garage with a set of poles and tossed them onto the beach chairs. The poles were bamboo, genuine bamboo, the kind used at luaus. She was still talking but he didn't make out a thing she was saying as he walked over to see what was wrong with the poles, nothing obvious, before going into the garage to help with a dresser that was tucked backed into a corner. She had already emptied every light bulb and battery in creation from the drawers. After dragging the old piece out to the driveway, he thought to ask what she wanted with the light bulbs and batteries. But then he didn't. Instead, he gathered his fishing stuff and fit it all into the back of his car.

The forecast was iffy. He didn't understand the urgency for clearing the garage. She wanted it emptied before tackling the attic. He wanted to hire a junkman, but she didn't want a stranger going through their things. Fine, he thought, no problem at all.

"Henry, look at this!"

He was standing in the driveway wanting very badly to dig for another cigarette when she rushed at him with something cradled against her body. It was her old equipment bag; first team All-American her senior year at Cal-Poly. "I can't believe this!" She was thrilled, the bag bulging at the seams. Unable to contain it, she plopped it at his feet. When it hit the ground, right off she was down on her knees ripping at the zipper, anticipating, hoping for something exciting. He didn't recognize the bag as any great find, none of it his. Lord knows what happened to his equipment, at least thirty years since he played in the beer leagues, maybe more, two, three games a week and then to the bar afterwards to get hammered with the guys. He played first base and batted sixth or seventh. He wasn't as good as she was, but he was alright.

The bag had her initials, J.S., and the Cal-Poly insignia; top of the line for its day but in its current state cracked and wrinkled and covered with dust. She rummaged through it and, after finding a glove and an old jersey, pulled out a bat, the one signed by her teammates and given her for making All-American. He watched her turn the bat in her hands. It was a real nice bat. He knew that. When they first moved into the house he used to take it out and swing it, full cuts in the garage when she wasn't around, a sure bet any child of theirs would be a talent. Before messing with the bat, he would thumb through the photographs that were stuffed in an inside pocket of the bag, taking his time with the ones he liked most, the majority of them action shots. He had the horns for the girl who played short, his full attention on her whenever he attended a game. He took note of the other girls as well, but none of them with the grooves like the shortstop. And then his wife, her grooves weren't bad either, back in the day. When he found himself at one of the team's parties, she was the first to approach him. What the heck, he thought. She maintained terrific grades. And he admired the way she covered all that ground in centerfield. She could hit, too. Boy, she could really hit.

He watched her pull the photos from the bag and try to bend each one flat to look at. "These are awesome. I forgot about these." Her voice was excited and it unsettled him. "It's Kat and Allie?" She angled a snapshot up towards him. "Do you remember Kat and Allie?" He saw the two players, cheek to cheek and covered in mud. He scrunched his face as if saying no, he didn't remember them. Then he turned from her. They were just old pictures.

It was damn hot in the garage, suffocating. She hustled her softball things into the house and he stepped out towards the street for another cigarette. When he saw a neighbor walking his way he changed direction for the only tree in the yard. The tree was drooped and in dire need of a trim. He inspected it until the neighbor passed. He wasn't going to talk to the neighbor. And he wasn't going to trim the tree. And he wasn't going to cut the grass, either. Then he stepped back and looked at the house, a modest house, yet from where he stood it blocked every part of the sky behind it. A cloud moved in front of the sun throwing a shadow onto the house, a big, fat, gray zero is what it looked like to him. He got a chuckle out of that.

He lit his cigarette and chewed on it some, the neighbor's name who just walked by not even close to the tip of his tongue, all the time people popping up in his sight, an imposition of the greatest degree as far as he was concerned, forced to think of a name he had no use for and didn't care to have to think about. He couldn't remember the neighbor's name and it annoyed him he was stuck on it so he moved his thoughts to fishing, a few work buddies going north, like they always did. This year he was going with them. He didn't tell the wife, but didn't think it mattered, because she would be spending the week with her mother. He drew in on the cigarette. The smoke filled him with a tickle, almost the sense to skip and click his heels. But then he remembered he was supposed to call Chantelle, the housekeep.

"What's with all the paint up there?"

He didn't know the wife was back in the garage. And he didn't know what she was talking about. "There … up there!" She was pointing to a row of cans lined on the top of a cabinet, a cherry- walnut cabinet he had made himself. The cabinet was empty, a cabinet she could never decide what to do with. So it was stuck out in the garage with a few cans of paint on top of it.

"Why are they up there? They're no good anymore."

He searched around for the stepstool, thought it was her idea to put the cans up there. After finding the stool, he climbed up and took the cans down and stacked them in a wagon he figured was trash, a tiny wagon they picked up from somewhere years before. He felt ridiculous to be stooped pulling it along, the cans weighing down the wagon and causing a squeak.

"What are you going to do with that?" She was jutted forward, perspiration beading her face.

"I'll take it to work."

"What?" She about popped a vessel. He didn't work anymore. Although it was not like he forgot. "I'll take it to the shop with whatever else you want to get rid of. They'll be happy to see me." Without looking at her, he pulled the wagon to the end of the driveway and left it on the sidewalk.

Then he walked back to the garage to find her sliding her hand along the cherry-walnut cabinet as if it were the first time she'd laid eyes on it. "This was a lot of work wasn't it?" She was just talking, so he didn't answer. She wouldn't want to keep the thing anyway. And he had no use for it. They could pass it off to one of their children; let them deal with the rest of the crap, too. But they didn't have children.

The phone rang. And she plowed in its direction. One day the end of her, is what he figured, the way she jumped for the phone. She found it near the steps into the house and brightened when seeing who it was. It was her sister. In his mind, the sister had it made, sold her real estate business for a home in Nags Head where she spent her time playing golf and tennis. Why she was getting married after all the years, he would never understand. Then he wondered if maybe the sister would want the cherry-walnut cabinet. Or maybe she wouldn't want it. He didn't care. Though he did know he wasn't going to stand there and listen to every inanity ever uttered. So he turned to go out of the garage.

"Maybe we should keep the wagon?"

He looked back at the wife. She was gesticulating for him to hold on a second. He jabbed his hands back at her; she was deranged, bona-fidedly certifiable if she thought he was going to stand there while she was involved on the phone. And then just like that, she was finished. She put the phone down and stroked the cherry-walnut cabinet. "What are we going to do with this?"

"We don't need it," he said. She slumped as if disappointed. So he looked at her like, what the hell? He didn't mean to be so gruff, but he was on his way for a cigarette, besides, the cabinet was only a piece of furniture, of no use just like the dresser they drug out onto the driveway.

"It sure is a beaut," she said, like maybe there were possibilities. Then she darted toward the thing and started moving the crap piled against it, all of a sudden, bing, bang, boom, shit in every direction. She pulled on a headboard and dragged it forward for him to lug out to the driveway. He didn't say a word, just took the headboard and tossed it with the other things. Next were a bedframe and shelving and wallpaper. He carried these things out without any sense of when he carried them in, when all was in front of them and the intervening years had yet to collect in the garage and in the closets and, only lord knows what, in the attic. Much of it could be salvaged. He knew that's what she had in mind. But he fancied more along the lines of discarding it all for a one-room basement apartment on a side-street in Sausalito, cable TV with Internet service and a street-level window to watch the legs walk by. The Travel Channel ran a weeklong special, up and down the coast to all kinds of places he'd never been. He couldn't have enjoyed it more if he were there himself.

When finished humping the unused bedroom stuff out of the garage, he returned to find rubbish and clumps of old stink-rags flung out from behind the cabinet. He could hear her back there grunting and panting.

"Henry?"

He stood there thinking, Christ, of all places.

"Henry, there are magazines back here." She squeezed out from behind the cabinet and came at him damp and out of wind. "These were stuffed into an opening back there in the wall!" She aimed the magazines at him, flipping through pages for him to see, each one revealing a tangle of naked people in various positions having sex.

"What were these doing back there?"

He looked at the pictures in such a way that he didn't really look at them and then shrugged as if lifting his shoulders was great effort.

She spoke again. "Where did they come from?"

"I don't know," he said. "Probably from the people before us."

The possibility didn't occur to her, but it didn't matter, she was engrossed with the erections and the gaping orifices, the pictures more frank than anything she could have imagined.

"Here, I'll get rid of them." He got hold of one of the magazines but she kept a grip on the others, stuck on the swollen purples and the shocking pinks. "Jeez, these people are really at it." She was trying to make light. But he wasn't going to stand there with her ogling like that.

He left the garage and dropped the magazine he had in the trash before walking around to the front door where he entered the house. The kitchen was a disaster, bloody butcher paper all over the counter and dirty dishes stacked in the sink. He kept his distance and poured a drink. At one point he offered to redo the kitchen, but she wasn't sure, so he never got around to it, ever since his skills eroded; the Phillip's-head and the drills, all of his tools put away. And there he stood the sink and the counter a pile-up of obscene proportion. Irking him most was the mound of paper dangling from the refrigerator, notes and receipts and expired coupons lurching out to paw at him. He had urge to pull them down and rip them to shreds but the letters, M-o-t-h-e-r, scratched on the calendar across the week of the sixteenth caught his eye. Only three more days and he'd be up north knee-deep in a mountain stream flipping for steelhead just steps from a knotty-pined, off-the-grid, simple, square of a cabin, fifty-five degrees, sun-splintered and not a god-blessed sound but the birds and the breeze and the riffles.

"Did you call Chantelle?"

"Damn," he bristled. He didn't hear her come into the kitchen. And she always interrupted his thinking. No, he didn't call Chantelle. And he wasn't going to call Chantelle. Hell, it had been an hour since they started clearing the garage and not a damn thing had been accomplished, a pain in the ass maybe, but that was it. If Chantelle was there, the garage would be finished and everything would be in order. Then she would take the wife by the hand to the guest bedroom where they could do each other's hair and discuss the magazines the wife found in the hole in the wall behind the cabinet. And he would be off the hook.

He dumped the rest of his drink into the sink and told the wife he called Chantelle but there was no answer so he left a message, one, two, three seconds, waiting for something out of her mouth before leaving for the garage. It was steaming out there. And the magazines were stacked on the steps leading from the house. He took off his T-shirt and tossed it onto the step to cover the magazines, immediately garlic and onions and bourbon reeking to high heaven. She followed him out and stood by him with hands on hips, not to be confrontational but just to stand there next to him. Neither spoke. And there were things everywhere yet to go through. But the quiet was too much for her. She couldn't help it. "When are you going to shave?"

He shook his head and scratched his armpit, a hairy, sweaty scratch. He didn't know when he was going to shave. He walked over to the wall he was facing and started taking things down, hoses and shovels and rakes and saws. He took them all out of the garage and let them go on the driveway while she retreated to an opposite corner. When the wall was cleared, he stayed outside and stood on the grass, the shovels and the rakes and the hoses and the saws indiscernible from the boxes and the crates and the sell pile and the junk pile and the maybe pile and the I don't know pile, none of it, in his mind, worth anything more than a hell of a mess to have to deal with. He had a hard time imagining Chantelle not around anymore, seven or eight years she'd been with them, immediately to mind, not necessarily how clean she kept everything but more like how she and the wife spent so much time in the guest bedroom braiding each other's hair and giving each other pedicures, and, how every so often, while peeking in from outside the window, he would see them with a hand on each other's cheek. One night he swore they embraced and kissed. It was titillating, though hard to tell through the curtains if that's what he really saw, Chantelle always in her ass-cracking shorts and skin-tight T-shirts. He liked having Chantelle around. And he wasn't going to be the one to tell her they were laying her off.

"Henry?"

The wife was on her knees fingering through a box. "What do you think about renting some storage?" He barely heard her and didn't answer, off in the grand, solitary world that was his head, behind the woodshed with Chantelle.

"Henry!"

He stumbled, turning his ankle in the grass, the same grass he once fawned over, thick, bushy turf he would bury face in. It filled him with vigor, sniffing the soil. But he hadn't tended to the yard for some time.

She saw him jerk forward as something flew off behind him.

"Are you okay?"

He didn't say a thing.

She was up off her knees and moving at him. "What happened? Did you get stung?"

He didn't know what she was talking about.

"You just got stung!"

"What?" He looked at her as if she were out of her mind.

"You just got stung!"

"No, I didn't."

"Let me see." She grabbed at him and found a welt on the back of his arm. "You just got stung!"

Since she mentioned it, his arm was itchy and burning, but it didn't really hurt and he didn't want her bothering. He pulled his arm away. "I'm fine. I'm fine."

"You need that taken care of."

He turned up his nose. "Do you smell something?"

It pissed her to no end, the way he changed subjects. Of course she smelled something—he needed to bathe. But there was a lump on his arm the size of a knob and it could get infected. She told him to stay still, she would be right back.

He knew what was next so he stood there and watched, a hell of a thing, the wife running off on his account, no clue as to what possessed her to do such a thing, and a real drain to be bothered with thinking about it, although he would dote over the children like that, knew it for damn sure, never able to sympathize with his work buddies about having to bend over backwards to please their kids. Shit, he would have given his left nut to have had the chance to bend over backwards for his kids. He clutched himself. And just as he was, again, back behind the woodshed with Chantelle, the wife came zigzagging through the garage with a tube of ointment and a bag of ice. When she lifted her head to say something, she tripped and fell.

He saw her go down. And he heard her hit. And in that drip of an instant the thought occurred to get in the car and ride, ride it hard out to Sausalito or Alaska or even Kansas for chrissakes, wherever he wanted to take it.

"Henry?"

But there was only a half a load in the tank and just a couple of bucks in his pocket, so probably, down to the corner for a cup of coffee would be as far as he would get.

"Henry!"

"Christ!" he groused. Then, realizing his callousness, he couldn't help but chuckle. He could see her hand just above the boxes, pleading. Right away he knew it was a bad one. She wouldn't be going to her mother's. And he wouldn't be going fishing. He walked over to where she was splayed out and told her everything would be alright. He said he would take her to the hospital. She said it was her hip. She was sure it was broken and thought maybe an ambulance would be better. He said that was okay and went for the phone.

He went into the house and, in the process of searching for the phone, tidied up the counter and moved the toaster over the bread drawer where it belonged. It was hot and he was thirsty so, while looking, he took a quick one. The counter was cleared but the sink was still stuffed and filthy. And the walls were peeling. And there were nail-pops all over the ceiling. The house would never go in its condition. He was sure of it. And the drink didn't do him any good. So he went back out to the garage.

She had inched herself upright and, as soon as he appeared, started pointing at the shelf where she left the phone. He picked up the phone and called the emergency service, hoping they would get there in a hurry, extra-glad she wasn't whimpering or crying out. She was a tough, old bird. And he was happy for that. He'd seen her go down before, a year after college and just before they were married, full bore around third base and then all of a sudden collapsing face first as if shot in the back. Her Achilles snapped. And she pretty-good banged up her knee, amongst other things. He thought she took it like a man, no writhing and moaning, and no minor injury back then either, a long while laid up.

"Henry, the heat is unbearable. Can you get me some water?"

That would be no problem, no problem at all. He went back into the house and looked in the refrigerator for a bottle of water. For sure, surgery would be required, and after that, at least a week in rehab. When he returned to the garage, the emergency service had arrived. June was strapped to a gurney and rolled to the ambulance. Too late with the water, he watched her go, and then, not one thought about the things strewn on the driveway, closed the garage and went in to find another shirt. It would be a long day of suffering and waiting. He would do the best he could, take care of the paperwork, hold her hand if necessary, anything needed. And at night after getting back home, he would shower and shave. Then he would call Chantelle. And hopefully, if he was lucky, they would paint the place.

Tom Quinn

Pam Baggett

SO MUCH

for my sisters

The beach boardwalk, where salt air collided
with the sweet grease smell of doughnuts
fresh from the fryer and pinball machines pinged
in the arcade. The Squirt the Monkey game owned
by friends' parents who gave us better prizes
when we won, not plastic pinwheels
but big plaid bears and hot pink snakes we draped
around our necks like feather boas. Benway's
Beachwear and Gifts, where bone-china cats
and spotted dogs nestled in our palms, fifty cents
for a family of three. Sugar Shack snow cones
in leaky paper cups. Spinning ourselves dizzy
on the Tilt-a-Whirl. The Ferris wheel that crested
over rows of nickel games, rocked at the top
in a breeze off the Atlantic as passengers climbed on
below. The wooden carousel, each of us astride
our favorite horse, mine black with big red roses
on her saddle. And the leaping dog I always
chose if we got a second dime. So much

to leave behind when we climbed
into our mother's car as if it were another
ten-cent ride, not knowing our furniture
would be packed, stuffed animals crammed
into boxes, frail china pets heaped in blankets
by the man about to become our stepfather.
We'd glue their legs on in a new house
hours from beaches and boardwalk rides,
no clue yet how carelessly he would break us.

Deborah Finklestein

PEDAL

His garage sale purchase—
an old peach bike.
Parked against the cracked
adobe wall. Pink rose
vines creep along stucco,
create webs over windows.
Inside, empty cabinets
match my belly and change jar.
We sit on corrugated cardboard,
eat free canned goods,
look out the window
at the lilac bush.
The wind dusts petals onto the air.
Like gently falling snow,
they cover maple tree saplings,
only feet from our window.

Deborah Finklestein

Deborah Finklestein

BEACH HOUSE

You said
at least it's not pink
as we entered
the weathered,
light green shack.
I always wanted to stay
in a red one
but each year we slept
in green pastel,
like leftover
mint chocolate chip
ice cream that had slept in the sun.

Deborah Finklestein

Elizabeth Stoessl

SHELTERED

How much better we should live in the old house today!
—Gaston Bachelard, *The Poetics of Space*

And how much safer too:
In the garden, gone
those gigantic gooseberries
and toxic tomatoes
we'd yank from dirt enriched with DDT
and stuff unwashed into our mouths.
The huge hollyhocks we'd pluck
for dolls' skirts would now be
sadly shrunken, missing
their banned fertilizers.
How clearly we'd see our feet
on the creek bottom, its water free
of runoff from the butcher shop upstream.

And inside,
the heat pipe from the furnace,
safe spot in tag games,
rose upward through the house
wrapped in layers of asbestos
protecting us from burns
as we circled it, caressed it,
its flaking particles
in our ignorance freely inhaled.
Asbestos now banned and gone
the way of the coal furnace,
sedans without seatbelts,
and shoe-store X-ray machines
where we'd gaze on glowing toes.

PADRONE

Paul C. Dalmas

The only place I can find to park is a block down the Vallejo Street hill, a block so steep that concrete stairs run up the sidewalk. It's a dreary San Francisco day. Low fog blocks the sun, and a long siren at the Ferry Building moans a warning followed by an authoritative, neighborhood-blanketing voice on a loudspeaker: "This is a test. This is only a test."

I begin the heart-pounding climb to my family's home, the Victorian that my Italian immigrant grandfather built from the ashes of the 1906 earthquake and fire. Its Carpenter Gothic details are gone, removed and stuccoed over for cheaper maintenance before I was born. By the time I reach the house I am puffing, sweating. Six more stairs to the porch. I turn the key in the left-hand door to my 92-year-old aunt's vacant apartment and begin the final climb, thirty-one more stairs with a polyester runner, a kitschy imitation of a Persian pattern—gold, emerald green and sky blue. My aunt loves that carpet.

The odors compound with each step: talcum powder, years of dust, a faint scent of urine. The apartment has been empty since that morning last year when my aunt called me.

"I'm feeling bad," she said. Her voice lacked its usual feistiness. "I gotta see the doctor."

From the doctor's office she went to the hospital, then—weeks later—to the assisted-living place where she will spend the rest of her life. She'll never make it up these stairs, never see her home—her parents' home—again. It's a change for me, too. I've gone from being nephew to landlord, and that's why I'm here today. I'm checking her apartment and the vacant one downstairs. What has to be done? What might it cost? I have to separate family from finance, sentiment from sense.

At the top of the stairs I pause to catch my breath, and my mind stays with my aunt. The big events in her week now are three visits to the dialysis center. That was where I saw her earlier this morning. She sat, her frail, shapeless body minimized by the black vinyl recliner, propped by pillows, warmed by blankets. She dressed up—a baggy peach sweater-blouse, a gold necklace, pearl earrings that drooped from her earlobes. Tubes red with blood run from the thin, papery flesh of her arms to a gray machine with a pump synchronized to her heart. A plastic bag filled with murky liquid hangs beside her. The nurse's remark is always the same: "Three kilograms today. Nice work." My aunt is the last of my mother's generation, I think. When she's gone, it's just me.

My mind snaps back to the job at hand, and I begin my assessment of the apartment's condition by moving down the hall to the bedroom. The rug is threadbare and patched with duct tape, the bed still unmade from the day I hurried her off to the doctor and the hospital nine months ago. A plush Mickey Mouse my daughter brought her from Disneyland waits on her pillow. An unwound metal alarm clock sits silently on her nightstand. The shelf of her TV stand holds a stack of decade-old *TV Guides* and an ancient VCR. Lobotomized by a power outage months ago, its timer mindlessly blinks twelve noon. Dust coats everything, the bureau, the powder containers and vials on her dressing table, and the gold-framed mirror above it. It's a family tradition, a superstition really. When members of the family leave for the nursing home—my aunt, her older sister, my grandfather—their homes awaited them untouched. Months pass, then years, and each apartment awaited a return everyone knew would never come.

In the living-room a couch upholstered in a faded floral print sags from years of use. I recognize the Cezanne print crooked over the couch: working class Parisians drink too much wine and dance away a bright Sunday afternoon. Not so different from my aunt's young life, I think, but I'm sure that to her the choice of the carved frame was more important than the artist or his subject. The end table holds a grimy glass dome containing an arrangement of silk flowers and a butterfly sealed forever in a vacuum. The room hasn't really been cleaned in ten years or painted in fifty. She refused to have help. I wonder what will become of all this. Am I a landlord or a nephew? What will it cost? Vacant and painted, the apartment is worth close to two thousand a month. Should that matter?

The dining room is the hardest to face. I remember the meals my aunt made for my college roommates and me forty years ago. She cooked for two days to satisfy her hungry young men, and the eating went on for hours. First cold cuts, olives, cheese and sour dough bread, then steaming plates of ravioli in red sauce. Next came the prime rib—always medium-rare—the mashed potatoes and gravy, the string beans, the tangy green salad. And finally a Saint Honoré cake—a profusion of puffed pastry, whipped cream and custard from her favorite North Beach bakery. Throughout the meal we drank glass after glass of cheap red wine. She fed us until we surrendered and staggered, groaning with gluttonous remorse, into the living room to drowse on the couch or floor.

The room still contains the same mahogany table with its six matching chairs, its buffet, its credenza. But now the Limoges china waits behind dirty glass, and space not occupied by furniture contains a confusion of things my aunt thinks are perhaps useful, perhaps important. She isn't a hoarder; she simply fears she might throw out something important. So on the table are years of telephone bills, P.G.&E. bills, bank statements, tax returns, stacks of old Christmas cards, hundreds of return-address stickers, an envelope containing twenty-two cent stamps. Around the table sit gift boxes filled with other gift boxes, an unused paper shredder, a bag of faded stick-on bows, a Cuisinart still in its carton, and, perhaps strangest of all, a stack of carefully laundered, ironed and folded rags in a brown paper shopping bag. Nearby is a sewing machine my aunt never learned to use and a hope chest filled mostly, I suspect, with empty boxes. Piles everywhere. Somewhere amid all this, she has assured me, is a stash of about twenty-thousand dollars. Her emergency money, she calls it. I have no idea where to begin looking for the cash. It's been safe here for a decade, I decide, so I shake my head and move on.

I hurry through the kitchen with its immense white O'Keefe and Meritt range and the tiny sink where she insisted on doing the dishes from her epic meals without help from my buddies or me. I don't want to think about the cost of a remodel here. New plaster, wiring, plumbing, cabinets, appliances. I know that the ceiling hides a live gas pipe that originally lit the building. It should be removed. On the wall I notice an electric clock that makes an arthritic whirring sound. Is it five-and-a-half hours slow or seven-and-a-half hours fast?

I step out the back door. Somewhere a neighbor is practicing his saxophone. The tune is mournful and unsure. I descend the creaking staircase to the apartment below, my grandparents' apartment where my aunt and my mother were raised. This second apartment, which has been empty for months, has an identical floor-plan to my aunt's above but resembles it in no other way. With the contractor's work immaculately complete, it awaits its next tenant. I smell new carpet (an expanse of beige) and fresh paint (shining white everywhere). I look at the plastic-laminate cabinets, a stainless sink, a fridge and stove both still stickered with labels from the appliance store. Here, in this transformed space, I am clearly landlord, not a nephew, not a grandson. The memories are vaguer, dimmed by the contractor's work. Yet I know the corner where my high chair stood, and the new range is in the same spot where my grandmother's pot of yellow polenta bubbled sixty years ago.

I wander from the back of the apartment to the front, from kitchen to living room. In the bathroom beside a new vanity and toilet, I find the only remnant of the apartment I remember from my childhood—a claw-foot bathtub that I correctly predicted would charm any new tenant. A week ago, when I showed the apartment to the young woman who leased it, I pointed out the tub. She loved it.

"It's so cute," she said.

The building's age, its high ceilings and ornate woodwork, have transformed it into something trendy, the latest thing. Ambitious young professionals from the Financial District a few blocks away are eager to move into the neighborhood. On weekends they trek up and down the hill, iPhones in hand, seeking the latest rental offerings from Craig's List.

I pass more quickly through the remaining rooms. They are empty and almost indistinguishable one from another. Dining room? Living room? Bedroom? I know which is which, but it really doesn't matter. Each gleams spotlessly and is carpeted in a practical, long-wearing looped pile.

Back in the kitchen I make sure that cleanser, Windex, paper towels and a sponge are on the counter. They're a reminder to the tenant to take care of the place, to guard her cleaning deposit. When I mentioned to her that the apartment had belonged to my grandparents, she nodded politely and smiled.

"Is the oven self-cleaning?" she asked me. "And the fridge. Does it have an ice-maker?"

The chirp of my cell phone interrupts my thoughts. It's my aunt, returned by van from dialysis to her assisted-living place and checking up on me.

"How's the place look?" She's talking about the remodeled apartment. We never talk about her place upstairs.

"I dunno," I say. "Okay, I guess."

"You gotta know for sure. You're the *padrone* now."

I shake my head. *Padrone*. It means *proprietor*, but the connotation is more like boss. It's a word I never thought anyone would use to describe me. There's no one else to take the title, so if that's what she calls me, it must be true.

"The place looks fine," I say. "Marco did a good job. Everything's fine."

I end the call and take a final look around. Nothing else to do, so I make sure the apartment, and its emptiness, are locked tight. Down the stairs and I'm back on the sidewalk, taking long strides down the hill to my car. I turn back to look up at the building. Behind the windows of my aunt's apartment, her tattered shades hang half-open and askew. In the new windows below, white blinds cut light to the refurbished rooms. I shrug and continue to my car.

The fog has cleared. The afternoon will be better.

GEORGE LUCKY

E.A. Fow

Did I tell you about when a devil tried to sublet my apartment? You think I'm joking; I am not joking. A devil left a message on my answering machine after he read my ad on Craigslist.

My friend Sally helped me describe my apartment in Brooklyn in four hundred words or less, with emphasis on the sunlight and not the four flights of stairs. I had to sublet it that summer so I could go to London to see Martin. He'd given me an ultimatum: if I didn't go, we would break up. I wasn't sure I wanted to stay together, but breaking up sounded worse. I had no summer classes, and perhaps if I had any great ambition or even a small desire to do something with my life, or had got off my butt and got an internship, I would have had a clear vision of what to do. I had no such vision, so I listed my phone number on the ad, but Sally warned me not to put my name.

The calls started ten minutes after I posted. I wasn't ready, and that seemed metaphoric, so I let the calls all go to voicemail. The next day I loved him again, so I listened to the messages and wrote down the details of people who wanted to live in my part of Brooklyn, but only for a month. It was a big decision: who would sleep in my bed and go through all my stuff? There were nineteen messages. If no one sounded right, the decision would be made for me. After the anxious sounding woman who needed to move immediately, and the graduate student who needed somewhere quiet, came the guy who had broken up with his boyfriend and had to move out, then the mother enquiring on behalf of her pampered daughter, but then a pause…a heavy pause, a breath, and then a voice oozed through the phone.

"Amelia," the man said, drawing out the syllables so far that they sounded wet. I moved my head away, not wanting the voice to leak out through the earpiece and onto me. "I'm calling about your apartment." The voice was deep, unctuous. "My name is George Lucky," he said. "That's right…Lucky. You should call me."

I was so skeeved that I shuddered and didn't write down his name. Then he said his number, and I didn't write that down either. There was another pause at the end of the message, then a long, deliberate intake of breath. Finally he spoke again: "Have a blessed day." Click.

The message had ended, but I could still feel his voice worming down my ear canal, and then it stayed flapping in there, like swimmer's ear. It was the oily, confident voice of an authority who would abuse his power as he saw fit. And he wanted to move into my apartment. I shuddered, and then I felt sick—he had called me by name. How did he know my name?

Another message began, but I was too alarmed to really hear it. I pushed delete but calmed down enough to listen to the next one. George Lucky was back: "Amelia," said the deep, oily voice again. "I thought you should know; I will move in right away." Click.

A very bad feeling spread from my stomach up to my throat. Sally would know what to do, so I dialed her, but her phone went straight to voicemail. My nausea was growing, and I didn't think I could speak without retching. I was going to hang up, but the phone started ringing in my hand before I could! The ringing was loud, aggressive. The phone seemed alive somehow. I just let it ring, counting on it going to voicemail, but it didn't…it kept ringing, and I started counting: nine rings, ten rings…eighteen rings, nineteen rings…twenty-three rings. With each ring, it grew louder, more belligerent, and the phone seemed to get heavier. I finally turned it over and pulled out the battery. It rang one more time then was silent.

I looked around my living room. I don't know what I was looking for, but what should one do in a faintly supernatural situation? It did help a little because everything looked normal, and bright winter sunshine was streaming in through the window. I walked into the pool of sunshine, my nausea receded, and suddenly I felt very silly. I put the phone back together, half worried it would ring, but it lay still, silent.

Then the doorbell rang. I knew it was him. It rang again and kept ringing... Then the phone rang, too, but it wasn't aggressive this time. It was soft, safe, and Sally's number was on the Caller ID. The doorbell got louder and louder.

"Sally?" The ringing was even louder now and deeper, as if my apartment had turned into a tolling bell tower.

"Amelia!" she exclaimed. "What's that infernal noise?!"

I had to shout, "It's the doorbell, it won't stop!"

Sally shouted back, and I thought she said something about George Lucky, but I couldn't hear her properly. The apartment seemed to darken.

"What?!"

"Why did you give him my number?" she screamed.

"WHO?

"GEORGE LUCKY!"

The phone went dead. The bell stopped, too. The silence was so startling it spurred me into action. I opened the window, poked my head out, and shouted down:

"You can't have my apartment! NO!"

A very ordinary looking man stood there, so ordinary that I can't describe him to you now. I was mortified—I'd just shouted out the window at a harmless stranger. But then he smiled and scared me.

"Really? I can give you anything you want," he said quietly, but his voice oozed all the way up to the fourth floor and slithered into my ear. I suddenly had no choice; I had to tell him.

"But I don't know what I want," I said.

The Devil shook his head in disgust then withdrew his words from my ear and turned and walked away. The offer had been revoked.

E.A. Fow

CLOSET PYROMANIAC

Jim Landwehr

I had the plan devised for quite a while before I actually garnered up the guts to carry it out. I needed the right time, place and, most of all, I needed to be alone, hidden. As sinister and morally suspect as the plan was, there was no possible way for a seven-year-old to conduct it in public view. It would have to be done undercover in a solitary place with no one around except me and my conscience. My quest for thrills and danger would likely only scare off siblings or, worse, lead them to squeal and thwart the entire plan.

My mother was a smoker, so I'd seen matches lying around the house all the time. It wouldn't take much to find a book of them and call it my own. If they weren't on the kitchen counter, they could be found in the living room next to an ashtray. If not there, then in the junk drawer or on top of the fridge. You didn't have to look too hard, and if you were a kid with a fascination with fire and nothing but time on your hands, it was a cake walk.

The matches were nothing special. They were the paper kind with the strike strip on the front. Eventually, as a safety measure, the strike strip was moved to the back side. One too many packs probably ignited in a person's hand when a wayward spark hit an unpulled match because they didn't follow the suggestion to close cover before striking. Because disposable lighters were not yet marketed, Mom sometimes bought a carton of matches that came with fifty individual packs. This insured that matches were never too far from the need for a cigarette.

I found the pack in the desk drawer in the living room. When no one was looking, I slyly slipped it into my jeans pocket. While my mother always said I was the easy kid, the good kid, one can only live up to that standard for so long. I sometimes made up for my goodness by being sneaky. In my defense, the sneakiness was simply an attempt to shield Mom from my wayward tendencies. Most times, it worked, sometimes, it backfired.

We were renting the house on Hubbard Avenue in St. Paul at the time. Having successfully escaped our years spent in the government housing projects, a stone's throw from the freeway, we were happy to be in our own place, even if it wasn't really ours. The "project years," as I like to refer to them, came about because of tough financial times and some marital difficulties between my parents. As kids, we thought it was high-living. We had our own cinder block patio, a communal swing set and a large common area courtyard between the twenty or so large buildings that made up the complex. Personally, between swinging on the swings with a towel as a Superman cape and chasing the mentally disabled girl around the courtyard, it was everything a kid wanted and a parent hated. Mom was glad to be out, and after we'd adjusted to the new neighborhood, so were we.

The house was a small bland A-frame with four bedrooms, no driveway and a small backyard. It was painted sad brown, with sorrowful beige trim. The smallest house on the block, it was set in a blue-collar, middle class neighborhood. We were literally four blocks from the

Kopper's Coke plant. I wish I could say it was the soda pop Coke, but it wasn't. It was a plant that produced coke by burning off the impurities of coal. This created a fuel that burns cleaner and hotter that is used for blast furnaces in the steel industry. The smell on the bad days was almost overwhelming. The plant exhaled atomic steam clouds three or four times a day. If the winds were from the north, God help us all.

With the matches tucked safely in my pocket, I went upstairs in search of a place to try them out. Mom was at work, and everyone else was either downstairs or outside. I went into the bedroom that Tom and I shared and looked left and right to make sure that no one was around. The closet was large and had two sliding doors, the sort where, if you slid one open, it overlapped with the other. The coast appeared to be clear, so I slunk into the closet, squeezed between the hanging shirts and clothes and sat down with my back to the wall, facing out toward the bedroom.

I pulled the matches out of my pocket. My hands fumbled nervously as adrenaline and nerves mixed and worked away at my heart. Fire was power, and I was about to unleash little bits of it one match at a time. I opened the cover and plucked the first one out of the front row. I'd seen Mom do this a hundred times, so I knew the routine. I put my pointer finger over the tip, and ran the match over the strike strip. It sparked and fired. I sat there, transfixed by the flame. It was amazing the way it glowed, soft yellow on the outside and a blue in the center. The flame never really seemed to sit on the match as much as envelop its perimeter.

I watched it burn until it was halfway down the match, then blew it out and put it in a slotted steel case that sat on the floor next to me in the closet. I wasn't sure what the case was for, but it made a nice holding place. Years later I determined that it was an air vent for the floor that was out of place. I pulled another match and fired it up. While it was strikingly similar to the first, I'd determined that it wasn't about the one burning in my hands, it was about the next one, and the one after that. Fire was my crack, and the pack of matches was my dealer. I held close to twenty hits in my hand and I intended to use them up. I was out to OD on fire.

The second match burned down and I blew it out and set it in the slotted container. It was clear I was alone and stood little chance at being caught in the act of my crime. The shirts, jackets and sweaters hanging in the closet made a perfect cover, and I was tucked back deep, so that only my feet and lower legs showed. I was disguising myself as a pair of my own shoes, only with lower legs attached. It was pure genius, and trickery.

I lit a third and then a fourth. They came more frequently as I mastered my technique. As I sped through them, I got reckless with their disposal. Along about the sixth or seventh match, I caught a yellow glow out of the corner of my eye to my left. I turned to see a fireball about the size of my fist coming from the steel container. My eyes bugged out. *Holy crap! Where'd this come from?* I blew a couple of long breaths at the blaze, giving it the oxygen it needed to reach its true potential.

I was paralyzed by fear as the fire gained strength, evidently fueled by the pile of half- burned matches that I set carelessly aside. The flames licked upward and ignited a bathrobe belt dangling from its belt loop. The fire raced up the belt like a fuse for the closet fire bomb. The ground fire was intimidating enough, so when this thing took to the air, I decided it was time to evacuate and save myself. I scrambled out and spun around to assess the situation, thinking perhaps it would be easier to extinguish from outside the closet. The flames licked from the belt to a neighboring shirt.

It was clear that I was in over my firefighting head and needed to get some help. I struggled with the thought momentarily, as telling someone would, in essence, equate to a full confession of my wrongdoing. *Maybe I could get some water real quick and put it out.* I hesitated, and then decided that my initial hunch was correct. The choice was simple: get help now or burn the house down and kill my family.

I raced out of the room and down the stairs. I found Tom watching TV and said, "Tom, there's a fire!"

"A what? Where?" he replied.

"Upstairs in our closet," I said, my voice trembling.

Tom jumped up from the couch and took off running upstairs. My sister Pat heard the commotion and followed Tom to see what was up. I stayed downstairs, paralyzed by the thoughts of how much trouble I would be in when Mom got home from work.

Downstairs, I did my best fretting and praying. I heard a lot of commotion between Tom and Pat. Pat said, "Go get some water!" I saw Tom scramble down the steps to the kitchen to get some. He ran back up with a big glass of water. I heard Pat say, "Is that all you got?" to which Tom replied, "It was all I could find."

After the failed water extinguish, I heard Pat say, "Get a blanket or something." A couple of minutes later, it was out. I mustered up the courage to go upstairs and check out the damage. When I got there I saw that Tom had taken the screen off the upstairs bedroom window and he and Pat threw out the items that were burned onto the driveway below. He then went and got a fan and put it on high speed to clear out the smoke. It was a messy scene, but it could have ended up worse, much worse.

I stayed downstairs until they had the area stabilized and the cleanup started. They each came down and let me know exactly what was on their minds. Tom started with, "Do NOT play with matches. Ever!"

I nodded my head and said I was sorry.

Pat was a little less forgiving. "What were you doing up there? Do you realize you almost burned the whole house down? You could have killed all of us. Do you understand?"

I nodded, humiliated by my own recklessness and dreading the hour when my mother would come home. Tom and Pat's punishment was surely just a drop in the bucket compared to what she would dish out to me.

I spent much of the next few hours hiding out downstairs, contemplating my fate and trying to keep a low profile. It was better to be alone than endure any kind of passing scorn from my siblings. Being the "good" kid, I wasn't used to the feelings associated with such a heinous act. I didn't like them and the best way to avoid owning up to them was to isolate, to hide.

As the five o'clock hour approached I, came out of hiding and waited at the window. When I saw Mom's car pull up, my heart started to pound. Earlier, Pat called her at work and told her about the fire and that it was out, but I greeted her as she walked up the front walk anyway, hoping to plea my case before my siblings cross-examined my argument.

"Hi, Mom. I'm so, so sorry for starting the fire," I said with heartfelt remorse.

"I know you are, sweetie, but I hope you learned your lesson. Do *not* play with matches!" She shook her finger at me. "You could have burned the whole house down." Her tone was stern, but comforting. The scolding was nowhere near as bad as I had spent the last few hours imagining. It seemed she knew how scared I was, but took the care to see that I was okay emotionally first, before she hammered home the message. It was her gift as a mother and a single parent. She had the ability to show compassion and concern in the same sentence; discipline and devotion in the same breath. She was an enforcer with a heart, a mother and father all rolled up into one.

ACROSS THE STREET FROM YOU

Raymond Luczak

We deaf people live across the street from you two. We do not know your first names, but we have figured out the most important thing already: You are hearing. The way you two talk to each other, without looking into each other's faces, is a dead giveaway. Hearing people are always afraid of being open with their words, their eyes, their faces. We notice such details because with each potential friend or neighbor, we search for any tell-tale sign, such as hearing aids discreetly hidden under the hair, or hands unconsciously fingerspelling out loud, or eyes constantly monitoring the action around them. You two are married, in your late thirties, tan and beautiful with bright white teeth and well-manicured nails; you look like you'd make fascinating friends, for you'd be the type to have traveled Europe several times.

From watching you discreetly through our front curtains, we both decide that you, Mr. Smithgow, must be a doctor, or a medical specialist of some kind; the way your hair is trimmed every week so that it never seems to grow at all is our best clue to who you are. You do not wear a suit or tie, but you do dress well, with clothes purchased from Eddie

Bauer and ordered from L.L. Bean; you probably wear this under a white lab coat at a hospital nearby. We have seen the delivery men press your buzzer, usually to no avail; they leave permission slips, and they return the next day, pick up your signatures, and leave your packages, often right out in the open, next to your side door. The fact that no one steals them makes us feel good about leaving a large city for a smaller town like ours. And you, Ms. Smithgow, must be a professor of archaeology or sociology at the local community college, but we haven't had a chance to check the course listings there to see if you do teach there. You are beautiful, with a nice strong jaw that's short of masculine; you have wonderful laugh wrinkles around your eyes. We wonder if you have children, but we see no evidence of toys, or young adults who resemble either one of you. No one visits you. Of course, we don't dare approach you. After all, we don't want to give the impression that we're nosy folks. We are your new neighbors.

The distance you maintain with each other is carefully gauged from the second you two step outside to the driveway. The distance never changes as one of you locks the house and the other unlocks your maroon Saab. In the car you two sit carefully, wearing seatbelts to prevent the two of you from ever crashing into each other. Your bodies have become no-fly zones where spontaneous affection is forbidden.

After you leave, we discuss you two, deciphering the nuances of your body language. We wonder if you two have observed us talking, laughing, hugging our new deaf friends when they park in front of our house. They inquire after you two and our other neighbors, but we really have nothing much to say. We are still settling in, what with many boxes left to unpack. We are also hectic with our new jobs, working deeper within the deaf community here. It is so much better where we are now, for we no longer have to strain our voices with hearing bosses and co-workers, and we find it hard to believe that we now own our first house. In the city where we once lived, we paid an exorbitant rent. No more, we agreed, when both of our job offers from this new town came a day apart. Fate, we decided; and left.

At five, we come home from our jobs in the opposite ends of the town, so it becomes something of a game when we hurry just to see who gets to park first in the driveway, and then on the street in front of our house. Sometimes when we arrive home at the same time, we kiss each other in front of our house. Then we find you two standing on either side of your Saab, scarcely looking at each other and walking past to the front door.

It used to be that hearing people would fret about the quality of our lives we led, demanding that we learn how to speak and use our ears to partake in the joy of their culture, but now more and more of them are learning to leave us alone, only because we are indeed happy to be as we are. Perhaps they stopped bothering us so much because they saw how well we could communicate, even bluntly, and how little direct honesty they have in their own lives. We wonder out loud about the lives you two must lead in that house.

Our first winter here comes. Everyone had warned us about the amount of snowfall, but we are happy, cozier still when we see the text announcement of yet another day of closings for schools and stores on television. We like staying inside with our fireplace burning so hypnotically, feeling our toes heating up inside the cocoons of our slippers. We can't stop watching the purity of snow heaving softly like goose feathers below. Back in the city, the snow always turned gray within an hour of landing. But up north, the whiteness dazzles our eyes nonstop, and both of our boys and their fiancées spend Christmas with us. They, too, remark endlessly on the extreme cold, but they also comment on the perfect combination of snow and Christmas. Our two boys, now in college, agree that everything has turned out amazingly well for us.

After we attend the holiday services at our deaf church, we come home, put wood in the fireplace, exchange presents, and show videos taken when the boys were young; we all comment on how their fluency in signs have changed since then. Their hearing girlfriends nod nonchalantly, still overwhelmed by the signing in our deaf church. It's clear that these women will never understand the very quality that has defined our lives. Our boys' eyes mist, knowing this, and we hug them without saying a word. When it is their time to leave, we stand out on the driveway. We hug our boys tightly, this time with tears. We wish they'd marry deaf women, but we know we can't control their hearts.

We look up and see the two of you bundled up in ski jackets and fashionable boots, waiting for that key to unlock your chilled Saab. Just before you two step inside and buckle up, you nod acknowledgement of our presence and wave.

We wave back with smiles. We do not go into our house until your car disappears down the snow-banked street.

The snow melts, and the full fragrance of spring makes our dog jaunty. We went to the shelter when, over our Valentine's Day dinner at a fancy steak joint, we realized how much we kept talking about dogs. That night we vacuumed and corralled our extension cords. The next day, after work, we were ready to adopt. The dog who demanded to be ours, with his alert eyes watching our signing, wagged his feathery tail and sat at attention in his cage. Then he flounced around, as if he wanted to show off his gorgeous spotted coat. He sat at attention, and we looked at each other. Within thirty minutes, we three were completely in love. We discovered quickly how much Leopold loved being brushed in front of the fireplace; we didn't know how much until we felt his throat purring, almost snoring.

We stroll together with the dog past eight houses down the street to the park, where there is a fenced-in dog run. Both the fence and the gravel are somewhat tatty, as the town hasn't had the money to improve most of the older parks, but then again, it's not quite time for outdoor repairs. In any case, we have begun asking around for a sign-friendly contractor to help us erect a fence for our backyard.

Once inside the dog run, we unleash Leopold. He sniffs and races after the other dogs. As we sit down on a bench, his new friends sniff us over. In the distance we catch sight of you, Ms. Smithgow, walking alone, clearly lost in your thoughts. You are wearing a bright blue windbreaker and a pair of boots, as some park trails are still muddy. We trade glances with each other. We want so much to ask you whether you are indeed all right, but you do not notice us. You go right by, disappearing through a matted cluster of trees that have begun their first growths of green. We wonder why until we remember the park's restrooms are over there.

Some dog owners come over to us and, in asking us which dog belongs to us, discover that we are deaf. Of course, they feel awkward with their mouths, hands. We are used to this, so we gesture which one. We clap twice, and Leopold stops, cocks his ears. We clap twice again, and he springs haughtily over to us. The dog owners are impressed, even trying to copy our signs. We scratch Leopold behind the ears, give him half a dog biscuit, and then he sprints off with his pack of friends again.

You return from the restroom. On the sidewalk alongside the dog run, you see us signing.

You do not wave.

We see the subtle glint in your eyes, as if you are ready to ignore us but can't; it'd be too rude. We stop talking and turn to you, ready to invite you somehow, but you are gone. We look at each other, wishing to absolve somehow the unsaid pain in your walk.

A group of our deaf friends from the city where we used to live crowds our house for the Memorial Day weekend. We are immensely touched to see how much they missed us. How good it is to see them all at once, and how delighted they are to see us; they can barely hide their envy at the spaciousness of our backyard as we barbecue ribs and serve beer. They are surprised to see our other hearing neighbors waving and gesturing clumsily from their backyards to us their simple gladness in seeing us having a nice time. It would seem to anyone that we have earned everything at last, but not quite. We live across the street from your house, which is now empty and up for sale.

Laurelyn Whitt

GHOST PAIN: 1840

Imagine the shock of the land
after the great removals:

for an entire summer
all but the mourning doves
were still,
their hollow, haunted sounds

draped the cypress,
hung stunned from
the sweetgum, the
sassafras.

It was a loss so complete
the massive sycamores
began flaying their
own bark, growing into
huge mottled bones.

Then over the southern pinelands,
something viscid spread.

Sticky on the red clay hills
staining the swamps,
pooling into sluggish
molten rivers

It flowed steadily west
where the Choctaw and
Chickasaw, the Cherokee,
the Creek and the

Seminole
        lay strewn.

*

It began that winter:
long tongues of pain
that stung & twisted,
a desolate, incessant
lapping

at something no longer there.

THIS OLD MINE

E.G. Willy

Cab stopped the Bagger 6000 mining tractor on a cinnabar rise, looked out at the brilliant sunset, and sighed. Lord, how he loved this place, this quiet expanse, these 30,000 acres of rock and subtle color. He'd loved it since he was a kid and had scrambled all over the place with the wonder that comes with youth. This place was him. He was it. Though he was alone out there on the mine, and though it was tough, he couldn't see himself being anywhere else. Still, he had a few visitors at the main house, the monthly meetings of the historical society, and then it was lit up like the old days, the old processing plant under the antique spray lamps, the greenhouse decked with trailing plants and fruit trees. It was quite a show, and Cab hoped that maybe he'd have a grandchild one day who would share the wonderment of this rugged terrain. Probably not. The mine was getting old. Even he could see it. There was still plenty of life left in the land, but in his father's time it had netted unheard of profits. It wasn't getting more lucrative as time passed. Loans were harder to get. Newcomers were arriving in hoards, setting up fancy boutiques and health spas. The taxes were so high that most of the mining sector was rendered undesirable. Cab figured he had about ten years left of operations before he was surrounded by newcomers and city tax codes. He'd seen his friends sell their land for quick gain and a tenuous hold on the future, older guys who flaunted their millions in bars, drinking their profits away in the nightmare of guilt.

Cab spied the trench at the bottom of the rise. "A hell and goddamn," he roared. "Goddamn and hell."

It was a newly cut ditch, the second in so many days. Someone had been out, sneaking around, messing with him. Just a week earlier he'd shooed a gleaner off his land, a young arrival who was digging around in the soil, looking for God knows what minerals. And now this.

"Freaking newcomers," cried Cab. "Slipper sniffers."

Cab got out of the mining tractor and strode across the brittle soil. The trough was still there, along with a few broken tools. Cab kicked a few rocks in, surveyed the damage. Not much. A trough roughly two meters in length. A joke really. The Bagger 6000 could clear that much in a millisecond. Cab mounted the mining vehicle, put it in gear, cursed loudly and headed to the northern periphery of his land.

Coming along the skirts of the Ascraeus Wash, Cab skirted the flat pan of broken stones by a good half mile. He stopped his vehicle, looked up at the rising Ascraeus. Rufus, his neighbor's protosaurum was waiting at the edge of the wash. He darted out, his tail swishing back and forth, his forearms pumping in reptilian challenge.

"You dirty dog," said Cab warmly. "You sneaky bastard."

Rufus hissed, advanced no further. His two hundred pound tail swept the red stones back and forth, sending up a cloud of silica. Though he was ancient by protosaurum standards, he wasn't to be messed with. He and Cab had run into each other a few dozen times, and on each occasion Rufus had near twisted him in two. The protosaurum wouldn't hurt a man if he stayed still. But it was a sorry fool who tried to resist.

"Where's your master?" asked Cab softly.

Rufus flicked a forked tongue, looked over his shoulder. Dirk Carson's figure appeared on the edge of the wash. He was walking with a cane, checking out the wash. Cab drove up, leaned out the window.

"How the hell are you?" asked Dirk. He now had a hand on the giant protosaurum, was fingering the giant reptile's collar.

"Working hard. Not pulling up near as much ore as I'd like," Cab replied. "What with these new restrictions."

"Me neither. It's getting harder every damned day," said Dirk.

"How's old Rufus doing?" asked Cab.

"Not bad, not bad. My only friend now for twenty-five years. I'm getting worried he might outlive me," said Dirk. "I mean, you're a pal and a neighbor, Cab, but ..."

"I know. Times are changing," finished Cab. His own protosaurum had died five years before. And the loss still was with him. It hurt him to even think about it.

"He's getting hard of hearing," said Dirk. "Doesn't see so good anymore."

"Just like us, goddammit," said Cab.

"Say, you see the mall they're building over there in Tholus?"

"Yep, the biggest mall on Mars. Or so they say," said Cab.

"I ought to go over there and blow a hole in that place," said Dirk. "That was the old Bernardi mine. The best, biggest, toughest mine on Mars and they've put a mall on it. What's this place coming to?"

"Well, we can't turn progress back," said Cab.

"No, you can't do that. Just me and you left out here. And there's no respect now. Not for us. Not for anything we've done."

"Keep on working. That's all we got," said Cab, then put the Bagger 6000 in gear.

"Catch you at the pancake feed?" asked Dirk.

"I goddamned wouldn't miss it," said Cab, putting the mining vehicle in gear. He headed northeast. Rufus watched him go, hissed a few times for good measure, then crept behind the shadow of the wash, waiting. Cab smiled. He didn't mind that Rufus was sneaking around on his land. He couldn't change it even if he tried. Cab and Dirk had once shared a beer there, checking their property lines. And when Dirk took a leak on the grainy surface, the deed was done. No matter what amount of bio-cleansing and retraining were attempted, Dirk's essence was now in the soil of the wash. It was the only thing that mattered to the protosaurum, its primitive brain unable to handle such concepts as invisible property lines and mineral rights.

"Jesus Christ, son of a bitch," said Cab as he descended from his tractor a few hours later. He stood on the corner of the northern parcel, looked down at the canyon below. "That slipper sniffer punk was up to something."

There it was, another trough in the ground, the same length and depth as he had seen at his previous boundary. Cab kicked a few pebbles into the trough and jumped back in the mining tractor. He knew there would be another trough at the eastern corner, but he still had to check.

There was a trough all right, the same size as the other two, and there was a fourth when he checked in six hours later on his southern boundary. Two slippers sniffers were standing in the trough, digging. Cab recognized the pimply complexion of recent arrivals, their skin not quite used to the Martian atmosphere, their balance uneven. One held a shovel. Cab recognized him as the same kid he'd run off a few days earlier, though now the kid had a couple of transplants in his cheeks and forehead, shiny, stupid crap college kids get.

"Goddamn and hell," roared Cab. "Didn't I tell you to get lost? And now you're back. This time you've made a big mistake, son. I gave you a chance the first time. I thought I was pretty clear."

"Sir," said the kid, holding up his shovel. "I'm here legally. I'm just checking on my property, making an informal assessment. I don't want any problems."

"Your property?" shouted Cab. He was already descending from the tractor, his big hands flexing. "What strange ideas are kicking around in your slipper sniffer head?"

"Sir, I don't want to have to ask you to clear off. I know you've got some equipment on my property... and your family has been squatting here for many years now... but as the rightful owner to this land, I'm allowed to perform an occasional inspection." The kid glanced at his confederate. The second slipper sniffer had his hands in his pockets, looked to be fishing around for something.

"Kid, time's up," warned Cab. "Prepare to be forcibly removed."

The kid brandished the shovel, said, "Mister, I'm warning you. I don't want to take action on this."

Cab had the shovel in his hands before the kid had time to shake it a second time.

"Hey, wait..." said the kid.

It was a quick blow, one designed to not permanently disfigure but enough to create fear. The kid squeaked, grabbed his already dangling hand.

"You shouldn't have done that, mister," warned the kid's pal. He held up the weapon he'd been scratching for in his pocket. It was a small stun gun, the kind of thing slipper sniffers bought when they arrived from Earth, the ubiquitous cheap safety device to defend against the "wild Martian" homesteader.

Before the kid could pull the trigger, his hand was broken too. And Cab was already crunching the plastic alloy gun in the dirt with his titanium shanked boots.

"Come on boys, we're moving on," said Cab as he threw the two slipper sniffers into the hauling bin attached to the back of the mining vehicle. The kids were too stunned to argue as they clutched their swollen hands, stared in disbelief. Cab found their vehicles behind an adjacent boulder, a couple of rental ATVs they must have picked up in Tholus. Cab casually put his tractor in gear, ran over them on his way to the road. The kids started to complain, thumped on the hauling bin with their unharmed hands.

"You shut the hell up," shouted Cab through the rear window, "or I'll take you out and finish you off like your bikes."

The hour drive to the Tholus road was in relative silence. Cab could see the kids in the back as they whispered to each other, not daring to look back at the older man.

When Cab dropped the slipper sniffers on the Tholus road, the kid with the implants had got up his nerve. "Mister," he said, his voice warbling, "I swear you're done for. You've trespassed on my land, assaulted me, ruined my personal property, and kidnapped me. I hope you've got good legal advice because I'm going to sue you down to zero. I mean it. You are toast."

"Kid, you can kiss this old Martian's ass," said Cab. "I've seen a thousand of your slipper sniffer punks on my land. You tell the sheriff when he comes by in a couple of hours you were lucky I didn't kill you."

"Mister, you don't know who you're dealing with. I'm going to reduce you to silt."

"Is that another threat?" asked Cab.

"No, it's the truth, mister," the kid replied.

Cab swung, caught the kid on the ribcage. The kid fell on his broken hand, let out another squeak.

"That's a reminder, kid," said Cab. "Stay off my land."

"Watch your back, mister," said the kid through a mouth of dust.

Cab hopped in the tractor, and, swearing and fuming, drove back to the homestead.

He spent the following day working around his house, moving things, getting stuff done that he'd been neglecting for months. It was a big house, made for times when families needed to be large and nuclear. Now it was too much for Cab. Soon the homestead would go to his son and his niece. Cab was sure both of them would sell it off. They were established back on Earth, were married to a pair of low-level idiot bureaucrats. They cared nothing for the monotony of Martian mines. Nor did Cab's brother want anything to do with it. He was an artist at the University of Acheron, a minor luminary, and he had long cultivated a snobby, easy way of speaking that hid his family's mining past. Cab's wife was out of the picture, living in Xanthe with a local real estate agent, it was just Cab alone. He hoped that maybe he'd have a grandchild one day who would share the wonderment of the rugged Martian terrain. But he wasn't holding his breath.

The house tidied, Cab got drunk, fell asleep watching a movie. He awoke feeling tired, and the Viscom was bleeping insistently.

"Are you sitting down?" demanded Gene Misuzawa, a fellow old school Martian, now Cab's lawyer. His image appeared in the living room, faded, came back into focus. He was in a soft leather office chair, was glancing over top of an iced drink, most likely a martini.

Cab smiled dully. Gene loved his martinis. "What's up, Gene?" asked Cab.

"I mean, you might want to brace for this."

Cab ran a hand over his face, said, "For what?"

"I just got a call from the district police."

"Something going on?"

"Remember running a pair of slipper sniffers off your mine recently?"

"What slipper sniffers?" asked Cab innocently.

"Oh, come on, Cab, I'm your lawyer. I don't got time to pretend here. This is real. I wouldn't be calling otherwise."

Cab nodded. "Yeah, what about them?"

"It appears you assaulted Byron Barrymore."

"Who the hell's Byron Barrymore?" wondered Cab.

"The slipper sniffer that's taking you to court, Cab," said Gene with a frown.

"What for?"

"I need to ask, Cab. Did you beat the kid up?" wondered Gene, lifting an accusatory eyebrow.

"I didn't hurt him, if that's what you're asking."

Gene held up a document, fingered it, and said, "Says here you broke his hand, bruised his ribs, gave him a concussion, and verbally abused him."

"He was on my land, digging in my soil, and brandishing a weapon. What was I supposed to do?"

"What weapon?"

"A shovel."

"The one you broke over his hand, or the one you slammed into his ribs?" asked Gene.

"Jesus, am I on trial now for running a slipper sniffer off my land? He was trespassing."

"I'm just pointing out the facts, Cab. The questions I'm asking are no more than what you are going to be asked in the deposition."

"I'm being deposed?"

"A week from now is what I have set up. You should be getting served any minute."

"You did what?"

"That's what you pay me for, Cab. I had to move quick."

"Jesus, what's this all about?"

Gene leaned back in his chair, threw a leg up on his desk. "I'm still working on it," he said. "But this much I can tell you. The kid's got a past but no money."

"Like every goddamned slipper sniffer."

"Does the Barrymore name ring a bell?"

"Nope."

"Hundred years ago his family were big-time actors in Old California. Apparently there were like five generations of them. Then things went south when the film industry died. And now the kid's trust account is shot. He's got two arrests for illegal synthezine. One for animal abuse. Some kind of dog fighting scheme. Did a few months. Three years back he went in the hospital for rehab. There's more, I'm sure. I've got my investigator, Freely, working on it."

"Lord," said Cab, worried. He knew Freely, an old school Martian. He was smart, quick on his feet, and a real nasty bundle. If you wanted dirt, you called on Freely. He didn't come cheap, though, and Cab reckoned he'd be paying more than he could afford.

Gene leaned forward, sipped his martini. "Right, I'll get back to you tomorrow. I can meet you for lunch at Z-Z's in two days. I've got a game of golf tomorrow with the kid's lawyer, Nancy Chew. I dated her a few years back, and I think I got a lot of credit. I bet I can shake most of what I need down on the first nine."

"Am I paying for that round of golf?" wondered Cab.

"You bet you are. The best damn round you never played," said Mizusawa cheerily.

"I'm glad to see you're working for me," said Cab, forcing a smile. A milky feeling was already filling his stomach, and he knew, in a deep, eviscerating way, that everything he owned and valued was going down the tubes.

The next morning the sun rose sharp and slicing across the Martian landscape. As Cab had his first beer on the porch, he gazed over the warm glow of the southern parcel as he had done now for seventy years.

"This is it," he told himself. "I am the end of an era."

He moved inside, had four more beers before lunch, ate a grizzly piece of bean cake, threw up, and settled into the bourbon for the afternoon. It was, of course, synthesized brew that made his scalp feel like it was being torn from the top of his skull by a vacuum, but it did the job. He woke five hours later, his head hanging wearily over the side of his couch. He turned on the Viscom entertainment channel, and with his eyes sliding sideways from intoxication, watched feathered apparitions dance across his living room.

There was a tap at his door.

Wondering who would make the three hour drive out to the mine, Cab opened his door, watched as a beaten up Tholus town car departed down his drive, a cloud of finely milled dust rising behind it in the evening atmosphere.

"A hell and goddamn."

The note, delivered the old-fashioned way, printed on paper, zip coded, and tongue fastened, had the scrawl of a man who still wrote like a child. Cab read it once, then again to make sure he had read right, and crumpled it up and threw it across the room.

"Crazy loony slipper sniffing punk," he said.

The note stayed on the carpet. The only thing that saved it from going in the trash was that it could be used as evidence. For two days he thought about the note. Even as he drove his tractor across the dusty surface of his mine, looking up every now and then to check the sky, making sure he had enough light to work.

The third morning, under the anguish of another hangover, he gargled a shot of bourbon and sat in the shower for forty-five minutes, sipping water from the shower head, blinking, letting the steam and soap clear the fog off his addled brain.

Z-Z's was full. There was a clamor of customers, mostly country clubbers, recent arrivals, sporting the slick pastels of slipper sniffer businessmen. Gene Mizusawa was at a table by the window, fondling a fresh martini, making unabashed conversation with the waitress. He saw Cab, lifted a perfectly scrubbed and manicured finger, and indicated for him to come over.

"Well, your ass is stirred and fried," said Gene. "What'll you have?"

"Bourbon on ice," Cab croaked, his stomach turning. He was already beginning to regret his order.

"You don't look so good," pointed out Gene. "Have you been hitting the sauce?"

"What's this about my ass?" asked Cab grumpily as the waitress disappeared through the shiny tables.

"Are you ready for this?" said Gene.

"Don't mess with my head, Gene. I don't have the time or disposition for it. Tell me what's up."

"Got news from Freely this morning. The kid's filed for title under the Immigrant Homestead Act."

"The Immigrant Homestead Act? Jesus, that law's been dead for a hundred years. And what's he got to prove? He can't take title over mine. I got the homestead. That much I know, by God."

"He can if he gave prior notice," Gene observed.

"How the hell can that punk give prior notice? He'd have to have been born almost two hundred years ago. And the last time I checked, time travel hasn't been invented yet."

"He's got prior notice," said Gene.

"What the hell kind of prior notice can get a man to go back in time?"

"Did you or did you not get a note in the last few days?"

"I did."

"Was it signed by Barrymore?"

"What about it?

"That's prior notice. Signed and sealed in non-digital, archival form."

"That is bullcrap, and you know it."

"But still a legal document," noted Mizusawa.

"What did your girlfriend Chew say?"

Mizusawa smiled weakly. "She told me even if I cut off both my legs and used my dick to crawl around on, I couldn't even make a case at the State Health Services. She says she only dated me because she felt sorry for me. She says it's time I quit representing old Martian families and get where the real money is."

"Goddammit! What is this bullshit?" Cab roared. Diners looked up, made muffled comments on the sort of the clientele the restaurant was catering to.

"Apparently the kid's got an ancient title," said Gene quietly. "Late in the twentieth century, it was customary to sell deeds to Martian Lands as gifts, kind of jokes. It was very popular amongst the middle class. You know, like gag jokes. Deeds were sold to anyone who inquired, all notarized, written up in the current legal jargon."

"Surely those deeds can't be valid."

"Not normally, no. But there were quite a few that were honored after the Emigrant Homestead Act, provided that the holder of the deed filed with the proper space agency."

"And he filed," said Cab flatly.

"No, he didn't file. But a family member did. As you remember from high school history, immigrant deeds were only honored if a continuous claim was filed. That way the land would still be in their possession when the frontiers people arrived. First you have to establish your claim..."

"*By marking the corners of your property with a minimum of four bars no less than two meters in length that can be detected by a government survey satellite or government documentary vehicle,*" said Cab, quoting the official act that had sparked Martian homesteading. It was an old story, known to every family that came to Mars in the pioneer years, an important part of their history.

"So you see?" said Gene.

"See what?"

"The kid marked your property with four bars. You as much told me the other day."

"They were scratches on my land," Cab pointed out, recalling the troughs the kid had cut at the corners of his land.

"The kid's got us by the balls, Cab."

"His visible markers weren't surveyed by government satellite. Those things fell to Mars years ago. It's all privatized now," said Cab. "That much I do know."

"So you admit there were troughs on your property?" asked Gene.

"Gene, what are you getting at?" demanded Cab.

"Well, I hate to tell you this, but Freely tells me your land was on last week's weather report. Four troughs, an anomaly. It was duly noted. Even the weather reporter pointed it out. All of Mars had a look at your property. As the satellite feed for weather is the only official government feed on Mars, well, we can't argue that point. The kid's got us on a technicality."

"What about the space agency?"

"The Barrymores filed in Kenya."

"Jesus Christ, you can't possible tell me Kenya had a space agency back then."

"Apparently they did. They had a treaty with the European States. There were several offices in Africa. And it's still a subsidiary of the African Space Mission. Strange but true, the last surviving agency from that period."

"Why don't you just tell me to get the hell off my land?"

"Now, hold on, we still have a few options," said Gene. "This African space agency hasn't been proven in court. We still got a chance."

"How much is this going to cost?" Cab said sourly, then put his bourbon to his lips and took a hard pull.

"This could be a long fight, maybe take you into the millions. Chew's firm is no lightweight. They could drain you dry. But I'm willing to go with it if you are. This could be a great case if you win."

"It also could kill me," Cab pointed out.

"You don't fight, you lose your land. If you do, there's just a chance you'll come out alive, maybe even keep the mine. You tell me what you want, and I'll litigate the living crap out of these people."

"This is bullshit, Gene. I'm paying to fight for what's legally mine."

"Good, that's settled. Now let's get some lunch."

"I can't," Cab went on. "I've lost my appetite."

Gene sipped his martini, said, "Turn over all your assets to a relative. I'll pull up the papers. We'll get through this. It's not my first slipper sniffer case. First you've got to play ball straight. You touch that kid again and we're done. Stay cool. There's still room to deal. Maybe he only wants a cash settlement. He could sign over the title, release continuity, anything that puts the rights back in your hands. He's the end of the line. Once he dies or waives claim, the property reverts back to you. And if Chew wants an early settlement, that might mean there's a hole in his armor."

"So I'll still have to pay for my own home."

"Cab, you know nothing comes for free. You just got to promise me you'll keep your hands off the kid. When he comes by again, you kiss his royal ass. You can't afford any mistakes."

"You mean he's coming by?"

"He'll be by all right. Tomorrow. For an inspection. The cat plays with the mouse before he kills it."

"I don't like this game."

"That's why you got me, Cab," Gene pointed out, smiling, showing off a new set of implants. Cab took a pull off his bourbon and shifted uncomfortably in his seat. Between his lawyer and the kid, there wasn't much room to move.

The kid came by the next morning, accompanied by his slipper sniffer friend. They were driving the same beat up old Tholus town car that Cab had seen departing down his drive. Cab gave the car a long look, wondered what back lot they'd pulled it out of. Clearly the kid was low on funds. That meant Barrymore's lawyer was taking this case on contingency. So there would be no room for a quick and easy settlement. They were going to bleed him dry before they took the homestead away.

"Damned lawyers are robbing us blind," said Cab under his breath.

He waited until they were on his porch before opening his door. Both kids had casts on their broken wrists. The Barrymore kid had his ribs wrapped. A pair of sunglasses covered a black eye. Behind them stood an overweight private security guard, another slipper sniffer. He had the same rusty complexion of the recent arrival, the peculiar sense of balance. Cab smelled the chemical odor of synthezine rising off their bodies and resisted the urge to twist the Barrymore kid in about five or six positions unknown to the human form. "Good morning, Mr. Barrymore," he said, "what can I do for you?"

"We've come by to take a look at my land," the kid replied. "I brought along a few witnesses just to make sure things are in order, that the borders haven't been shifted, and that you won't try to assault me again."

"Don't worry about it, kid," said Cab warmly. "Your borders are still there. And I won't hurt you. I will, however, tell you what's on my mind. You're a slipper sniffing little prick. I thought I should let you know that, although I get the feeling you've heard that one before."

"I must advise you that everything you say is being recorded," said Barrymore.

"Well, in that case, you're friend here is a prick too," Cab replied.

"Have you moved any of my markers?"

"No, nothing's been shifted. Your shovel's just where I left it, Mr. Barrymore. Please feel free to look around."

"We don't want to get in your way," offered the kid's pal.

"Trust me, son, you'll know when you're in my way," Cab replied.

"Then you won't mind if my friends and I check the processing plant too?" asked Barrymore, bobbing his head, letting his eyes slide under the lids.

"Listen," said Cab. "I know I treated you a little rough last time you were out here. I apologize. You have to understand I get a lot of people snooping around. It can get dangerous out here on the mine. There was nothing personal between you and me. You can have the roam of my land. Go anywhere you want."

"My land," corrected Barrymore.

"Well," said Cab. "I'm still here for the moment. And you aren't the first slipper sniffer that came around here. Probably not the last."

"By the way," asked the kid, "what is it with this slipper sniffer thing? I've been called that like a thousand times since I got here."

"That's you, kid," explained Cab. "See, when the first generation of immigrants arrived, they were so damned poor that they were going up on miner's porches, stealing their shoes, sniffing around for things to get their hands on. It ain't any different now. Just now you have a little money in your pockets and the law on your side. But you're still slipper sniffers. That hasn't changed."

"This is my land," observed Barrymore. "I'm not taking anything that doesn't belong to me."

"Then you don't mind if I don't come along. I got business to take care of here. Hanging out here with you guys is kind of making me sick to my stomach."

"I hope you have a place to stay after this is over," warned Barrymore. "I wouldn't want to think you were out here all on your own, no place to go."

Cab opened his mouth to speak, counted to three, then let his breath out. No sense in jeopardizing his case. The deposition was in a week. He didn't want to blow it now. He smiled, then retreated into the darkness of his home. Outside, the men got into their vehicle and began pulling across the roughhewn driveway.

Cab sat in his living room and drank a beer. "Goddamn slipper sniffing punks," he said to the empty house.

The first call of the morning was Gene Mizusawa. The lawyer was sitting in a bar, had his arm around a young woman. He was, Gene noted, wearing a brand new suit, had the look of a slipper sniffer about him.

"Jesus, Cab, drinking already?" asked the lawyer.

"I could say the same for you," noted Cab.

"This is lunch," said Gene, then raised his martini glass. "By the way, the Barrymore kid and his flunkies should be there right now. You aren't doing anything stupid, are you?"

"They're already sniffing around the property. I'm just sitting here being good."

"Excellent. And remember, we have the deposition coming up. I want you in fine form. No swearing. None of the tough miner stuff. We have to make you look like the injured party."

"No problem."

"There's another thing, Cab. About my retainer... well, it's not enough. Fees have gone up since we last did business. Do you think you could make a deposit in my account to cover expenses?"

"Yeah, I'll get right on it," said Cab, wondering how much of his money had gone to buy his lawyer's new slipper sniffer suit.

"Buddy, you don't look so good. You look like you need a little rest," said Gene, then gave the young woman at his side a squeeze.

"This ain't easy."

"I feel for you, brother," said Gene.

"Thanks, man."

Gene rang off, and Cab had another beer.

He got the second call when he was on his way outside to check on the processing plant. Barrymore's face appeared in the living room. His sunglasses were off, and he had a strained look, as if her were in great pain.

"Mr. Barrymore," said Cab.

"Hi, man, I'm sorry to bother you. But we got a problem here," said the kid, his speech slurred from synthezine. "See, our car broke down, and we're not sure how long a walk it will be to get back to the road."

"Why should that have anything to do with me?" asked Cab.

"Well, we're way out here on my land," said Barrymore stiffly. "And we'll need some help getting back."

"Kid, I'm not a private taxi service," observed Cab. "I'm the guy you're suing, remember?"

"Thing is," said the kid, "None of us have enough money for that kind of help. I mean we're like out a long ways. If you wouldn't mind coming and getting us, it being your mine and all. You are kind of liable."

"So now it's my mine?" queried Cab.

"I was hoping we could keep this as friendly as possible," said the kid. "And besides, what happened to that old frontier hospitality everyone is always talking about?"

"Kid, you slipper sniffers killed any left," said Cab with a sigh. And even though his innate resistance told him not to help the kid out, Cab moved to the display of the satellite feed he kept on the homestead wall, checked the location of the kid's car.

"Uh, man, what are you doing?" asked Barrymore.

"Kid, you stay right there," ordered Cab.

"Then you'll get us."

"Well, goddammit, someone is going to have to," said Cab. "Just stay in the car. Don't go walking around. I don't want to have to drive all over hell and back."

"Thanks a lot."

"Stay in the car, kid. I mean it."

Cab drove the truck out to the periphery. It was a good hour's drive, and the land was aglow with the dust of a wind coming in from the west. When he got to the place where he'd located the Barrymore car, he saw not one but two vehicles, then the two air rescue transport floating higher up in the atmosphere, sirens. Cab thought maybe he'd forgotten to say something. Or the kid hadn't taken him seriously when he said not to get out and wander around. As he got to the edge of the Ascraeus Wash, his neighbor, Dirk Carson, came running towards the truck.

"We've had an accident down by the wash," said Dirk, his words rushed. "Rufus attacked a couple of men. It doesn't look good. Too late for an ambulance."

"Ah, Jesus, no," said Cab. He got out of the truck, put a hand over his eyes to shade the sun. He could just make out the partially buried remains of the three slipper sniffers on the rocky surface of the wash. Rufus, Dirk's protosaurus, was hissing, bobbing, his great tail swinging back and forth.

"Goddamn, I told them not to get out of the car," said Cab.

"Looks like Rufus was waiting for them," said Dirk. "I should have kept him inside today."

"And they decided to resist," noted Cab dryly.

"They're slipper sniffers. How could they know?" said Dirk, worried.

"I think I was pretty clear in my warning, Dirk," said Cab.

Dirk put a hand to his face. "And now there's going to be all kinds of inquiries. Hell, I don't know what to say. They're probably going to insist I put Rufus down. My best friend for twenty-five years. And now this..."

Cab closed his eyes for a moment, made a mental note to refile his claim to break any remaining legal continuity the Barrymore family might have. "There was nothing you could do about it, Dirk," he said slowly. "They were all three high on synthezine. And one of them had a history of animal abuse. I warned them not to get out and walk around."

"What about Rufus?"

"Rufus isn't going anywhere. I can assure you of that. I have a record of the fact that they attacked me the other day. Probably did the same to Rufus. Violent interlopers. Goddamned idiot slipper sniffers," said Cab, trying not to smile.

Renee Ruderman

HOME WORK

My mother moved paintings, furniture
    late at night in her red robe,
long hair in thin strands down her back,

head tilted like a Modigliani portrait,
    while frames blonde, light,
and chair legs marched into new positions.

Her warm milk cooled in the kitchen.
    It was not decoration she was after;
rather stations for her restlessness,

to create a museum of hope, or, at least
    of questions, for when the patrons woke up.
The Cézanne print she'd hung in the hallway

was replaced by a lively Brueghel feast,
    and two chairs from the dining room
made their way to the piano

as if one page turner would sit left,
    one listener on the right. She would have
played a Schubert Lied were it not

for the way the notes spiraled upstairs.
    In the morning we lived in a house
not quite our own; night visitors

had rearranged the landscape. But
    we understood the fever of the familiar
and knew that moving

was what she had to do
to shuffle regrets
to stage the darkness.

Eric Weil

THE LAST PIN IN THE MAP

On the wall, my world map's continents
bristle with colored pins. I'd like

to stick more in, but I'm skin and whiskers,
slowed by time, soon to die in this place

that warrants no pin because familiar views
go unseen, the mind overcast. Photos jam boxes

on the guest room closet shelf. I sent postcards,
brought home scarf, sweater, shot glass,

coffee mug to dust or store or give away.
I rise on my cane, touch a blue pin on the shore

of a distant sea. I slept there, ate—something.
My finger wanders to a far-off blank,

for I have saved one black-headed pin.
Scatter my ashes. Right there.

Eric A. Weil

Carol Gloor

EMPTY NEST

Miracles await at workday's end:
National Geographic open to exactly the page
I left last night for my dreams;

kitchen counter flecked
with only the crumbs I spilled;

floor smooth and free
of the small dirt that comes
and comes and comes from many feet.

My dog and cat grow huge-eyed, sleek, complacent,
fur quiet in the belly of my shining house.
My spider plant springs towards sunlight
dangling more offspring than ever before.

We have sex in the bedroom with the door open,
or on the living room floor,
the only clutter, the only clamor,
our own.

Carol Gloor

THE LORD AND THE GRAND OLE OPRY

Gayle Compton

My mother had a bad feeling about the little house from the day she laid eyes on it. She reckoned she'd have herself a good long talk with the Lord before she set foot in it. Although she spent a good deal of time on her knees seeking counsel from the Almighty, I think she knew, deep down, that my father would have the final say-so in the matter.

I was a towheaded boy of six the summer of 1951 when my father loaded my mother, my two-year-old brother Orville and me into the cab of a borrowed truck, and with cook stove, washing machine, bed springs and six live chickens jouncing in the back, drove from Ashcamp to Ferguson's Creek, Kentucky. It was just one of the many times we had to pack up and move during Dad's career as a coal miner.

Our new home was tucked in a valley at the foot of Town Mountain, just around the curve from Greer Iron and Metal and the Pike County stockyard. It was an unpainted 10-dollar-a-month shotgun shack built out of hard luck and rough sawmill lumber. The long front porch, which faced the road, was the only part of the house that rested on solid ground. The living quarters, three rooms laid end to end, was propped up on "stilts" and stuck out over the creek bank at an imposing elevation. Mother complained of "dizzy spells" every time she threw dishwater out the kitchen window. Not long after we'd moved in, one of the props worked loose and set the house on such a tilt Mother had to scotch the dishes to keep them from sliding off the table at dinnertime. Dad said a man couldn't pour himself a whole cup of coffee without running it over. Otherwise, he didn't seem to mind that the house was listing 30 degrees out of the horizontal. He saw it as an opportunity to show off his coal miner's ingenuity.

"Stand clear, boys!" he'd say, hitching up his britches. "Looks like we got us a timber walking on the tramway. Top's working clean to the face. We either crib'er up or pull the man trip."

Indoor plumbing was out of the question, at least for us in those days. Our new home came with an outdoor privy which, as far as privies go, might be considered upscale. Designed by the same architect that built the house, it too faced the road, squatting over the creek bank on two hickory poles. Thus situated, it had its own maintenance-free disposal system, regularly and efficiently sending its burden to folks downstream. It was the type of facility commonly referred to as a "two-holer," equipped with snobbish side-by-side seating, a cozy arrangement with company in mind. Instead of a door, a foreshortened burlap flap swung on four rusty nails and had a way of fanning out and curling up, whether there was a breeze or not. This amenity obviously came with the assumption that the occupant wouldn't mind sacrificing a little privacy for good ventilation and view. Many a time, upon returning from a visit to this little retreat, Dad was heard to remark that "the man that built that Johnny barn sure knowed what he was doing."

Ferguson's Creek in those days seemed to be the most storm buffeted community in Eastern Kentucky. When the winds came, Mother could be seen scurrying about, pulling down windows, closing curtains, propping furniture against the door, chewing her fingernails and praying. Dad, meanwhile, could be found hunched over his little portable Emerson radio, a Camel hanging out of the corner of his mouth, trying to bring in Nashville.

"Oh, Lord Jesus, what on earth are we going to do?" Mother would whine.

"Let'er rip!" was Dad's reply, turning the volume up on the radio.

"But, Ted, honey, it could blow this little house away."

"It's been here a hundred years. I reckon it ought to be good for another hundred. Let'er rip!"

Occasionally, Dad would feel sorry for Mother, or else grow tired of hearing her mouth. Losing no time, she would snatch a quilt, curtain or whatever came handy and throw it over my little brother and me. Dad, bare-headed and shirtless, would open the door and yell, "Water on number 3 belt head. Man the pumps!" Then the four of us would make a dash for our 1936 Ford coupe where we'd huddle until the storm was over.

The storm never failed to work its magic on my young imagination. The gentle rocking of the car, the crashing thunder, the lashing, blinding lightning and the sea-like spray of rain against the windows conjured up a pantheon of heroes from my mother's bedtime stories. The old Ford became the "beautiful pea-green boat" as I went to sea with the Owl and the Pussy Cat. I became Jim Hawkins in the apple barrel bound for Treasure Island. I was Sinbad the Sailor adrift in a wooden bowl.

Mother, meanwhile, kept her head bowed, lips moving in silent and fervent prayer. I knew she was asking the Lord to have mercy on us and our little house.

Firing up another Camel, Dad would peer through the windshield at the writhing sycamores, swaying buckeyes, and the tall Balm of Gilead and remark with perfect calm that a good little shower like this sure helps the corn. Then he would turn on the car radio and go to fumbling with the knobs trying to tune in WLAC.

I had an uncle whom Mother found even less sympathetic than Dad during stormy weather. She often said that it was by the mercy of God that lightning didn't strike our house and kill us all on account of the way Dad's brother John Lester carried on when he came bringing his bottle and his guitar. John was always drinking a little, abundantly happy and celebrating, having gone AWOL or been let out of jail. He was mighty careful about where he left his bottle because Mother was liable to sling it in the creek or pour the whiskey down the toilet hole. Therefore, after a surreptitious long drink, he would put me in charge of the remainder with instructions to "hide it from your mother." Sliding the foul smelling bottle under my shirt, I'd sneak out to the coal house where John knew exactly where to look when his throat got dry.

Dragging up a chair, he would take the guitar upon his knee, get a faraway look in his eye and begin to tune and chord and fret, twisting the keys and walling his eyes. He was mighty particular when it came to tuning the guitar. It had to be in just the right chord. John was a professional. He was not one to settle for the key of G when he wanted a B flat. Biting his tongue, he would slide match sticks under the strings, start off in high hopes, stop suddenly and shake his head. Sometimes, he'd have one of us bring him a fine-tooth comb, a teaspoon or one of Dad's work socks to bind down the strings for just the right effect.

When he finally got things to suit him, he would throw back his head, roll his eyes in a great passion and his rendition of "Missing in Action" would bring tears. Another twist of the keys and he'd segue to "Mule Train" or "Bilin' Cabbage Down," patting his foot until the table rocked.

John played holding the guitar behind his back, between his legs and over his head, never missing a beat. He would sing awhile, then kick off his shoes and dance awhile. He would have everybody just busting a gut—everybody but Mother. He would keep up such a racket that at times even she would forget about the stiff weather outside. Every now and then the thunder would join in like a bass drum, lightning would knock the lights out, or the wind would blow a washtub off its nail at the side of the house and send it rolling and bouncing across the road.

"Please, John," Mother would plead. "Play us a good sacred song."

When the tempest was at its height and Mother on the verge of a nervous breakdown, John would fling open the door, shake his fist at the skies, curse the lightning and double dare it to strike him.

By and by he would get to missing a special guitar pick he reckoned he'd dropped somewhere on his way in. He couldn't hit another chord until he found that pick. Ducking his head against the torrent he would disappear into the night. In less than five minutes he would be back with a fresh guitar pick, wet as a muskrat and happier than before. Assuming a humble and pious manner, he'd lend his best voice to "Just a Closer Walk with Thee"—dedicated to Mother.

We were lying in bed listening to the Grand Ole Opry the Saturday night the house fell. Mother and Dad were in their old white poster bed near the front door. Grandma Fleming had come in from Coal Run on the Greyhound bus and was spending the night. She had taken the little cot belonging to my brother and me. Having eaten five ears of pickled corn before turning in, she was snoring like a contented sow. Orville and I were sharing a blanket on the floor keeping company with the mice, roaches, spiders and other boisterous creatures of the night.

Since long before dark, Mother had been nervously monitoring the weather. She watched the trees tossing restlessly in the warm breeze, the leaves turning their bright undersides. Ominous black clouds gathered over the mountains like a council of angry gods. Lightning rent the skies and thunder rumbled menacingly over the valley. Hours later, propped on a pillow by the window, Mother watched the billowing curtains, saw smoke blow down the chimney, heard the whistling of wind through the cracks and the groaning of old timbers.

"It's working up a good one," she said, trying to sound brave. "Ted, you ought to turn off that old radio..."

It was no ordinary thunder that drowned her words, but a sound of splitting rails, thunder that shook the earth, rolling and bumping over the mountain as though the fearsome Thor himself were riding the heavens in his iron-wheeled chariot. Lightning turned night into day. Rain came down on the tarpaper roof like pitchforks.

"Oh, Jesus, dear Jesus!" cried Mother.

About ten minutes later she became aroused by another sound—water dripping on the cook stove.

"Teddy, I hate to mention it, but it's sprung an awful leak in the kitchen. There's water running down the stovepipe..."

"What do you want me to do, woman, get out and patch the roof in this weather? Set a tub. I'll catch my bath water."

Once more Dad turned his attention to the radio, which by now had become a jumble of static and electrical havoc. "Avalene," he said, raising up on one elbow and trying to make himself heard above the thunder, "would you care to crank that radio up a notch? I'd like to hear a little bit of Wayne Raney."

"Ted, I've always heard it's dangerous to play a radio when it's..."

Thunder and lightning. Wind screaming like a panther.

Lefty Frizzell was whining, *"If you've got the money, honey, I've got the tiiime...!"*

More thunder and lightning. Forty-watt light bulb blinking.

"Turn it up. Turn that thing up!"

"We'll go honky tonking, baby, we'll have a time..."

"Turn it up, dad burnit! Tennessee Ernie is coming on in a minute. I'd like to hear 'Shotgun Boogie,' if you don't mind."

"We'll take your Cadillac and leave my old Ford behiiind..."

"Lord, help us all!"

Suddenly, the radio slid off the night stand, shot across the room and shattered against the wall. A framed picture of the Good Shepherd above the chifferobe spun on its nail and clattered to the floor. A chest of drawers tilted forward, all the compartments sliding out like cards in a deck. There was a commotion in the kitchen that must have been the Maytag washing machine or the coal cook stove heading over—or both—followed by a massive breaking of glass. Cans, bottles, fruit jars, pots, pans and buckets were rolling in every direction.

Grabbing onto a leg of Grandma's cot with one hand and my little brother with the other, I held on for dear life. I felt the house move on its foundations and heard Dad yelling, "She's falling to the drift mouth, follow the gob rats!" Mother was screaming something about the end of time. After that, it was everyone for himself.

The little house groaned as though in pain, lurched forward, shifted sideways, swayed drunkenly on its crutches then headed backwards into the troubled waters of Ferguson's Creek.

It was only minutes, but it seemed hours, before there was a sign of life among the wreckage—only the sound of wind and pouring rain. My first realization was that of being trapped in absolute and suffocating darkness, a condition which persisted until I managed to extract my head from the mouth of a large butter churn. With some help from the lightning I found my brother nearby, unhurt but badly scared. He was hunkering in the remains of the coal bin, a wet and blubbering Tar Baby.

Through the veil of rain I made out the figure of my father. Naked, except for a pair of plaid drawers, he was fairly swimming in what remained of some 40 Mason jars, an explosion of pickled beets, blackberry jam, sour kraut and apple butter. He appeared to have been scraped from one end to the other with a cabbage grater and thrown in the stew, which indeed he had, come to think of it. Seldom had I heard my dad swear. He was a man who stoically bore pain and hardship without the relief of profanity, except for an occasional expletive upon hitting his thumb with a ball peen hammer, cracking his head on the door facing and the like. Until now, I had doubted his capabilities in the medium. However, as soon as he got his jaw working, he gave tongue to some language not heard in church.

Meanwhile, Mother was nowhere to be found. With lightning dancing about his head, Dad scrambled to his feet and began searching frantically in the maze of broken timbers and tumbled household furnishings. I could see him plain—his wild eyes, his sour kraut and jam smeared face—a visage of anger, confusion and worry rolled into one.

"Has anybody seen my damn britches?" he stammered at last.

Mother appeared, miraculously, head poking out of an old hair truck wearing a leopard skin lamp shade like a Sunday hat. Seeing the three of us, alive and whole, she made for us with open arms, heading, pitching and thanking the Lord.

Another stirring among the rubble, and Grandma could be seen unrolling her bed covers and rubbing her eyes. Somehow, her bed had landed upright and became buried under a harmless avalanche of quilts, blankets and laundry. She had slept through the whole catastrophe and woke thinking it was all a nightmare. She allowed she was going to have to lay off that pickled corn. When it finally dawned on her that she was the victim of a real calamity she was fighting mad. She swore she would never spend another night with us as long as she lived. She said we were the rowdiest bunch she had ever had any dealings with.

It was only after the storm passed and neighbors came bearing lanterns, ropes, spirits of ammonia and personal commiseration that we began to comprehend what had happened.

A kindly gentleman carried my brother up the creek bank on his shoulders, I following behind hanging onto his belt.

Grandma refused all assistance and marched up the bank on her own, mad as a hornet. She told us what she thought about Ferguson's Creek. She told us where we could put the little house. She said she was heading straight for Coal Run where people were halfway civilized.

It took my father and two other men to haul Mother to safety. She had sustained little physical damage, but her nerves were wrecked.

"It's all on account of that old wicked music!" she said, wringing her hands. "That Saturday night frolic is the cause of it all. I tell you right now, I'll never listen to that old devil's music again the longest day I live!"

Dad paused, his face clouded with concern. Standing in the rain in his boxer shorts he looked out upon the wet and dismal night. He surveyed the sad remains of our home and the bare and muddy creek bank where the little house once stood.

"I think it's a crying shame," he said, shaking his head sadly. "We've done and missed the Grand Ole Opry."

BLUE DOLLHOUSE

Beth Copeland

People fight over crazy things when they're going through a divorce: Tupperware, pet tarantulas, Atlanta Braves tickets. My ex-husband and I argued more about who would keep a dollhouse than about who would keep the four-bedroom house we lived in. The dollhouse was a three-story Victorian he had painstakingly assembled from a kit. It had taken him longer to complete the dollhouse than it had taken the builders to finish our suburban home.

I had wanted a dollhouse ever since I was a little girl. As I child I turned cardboard boxes and dresser drawers into dollhouses, making furniture from match boxes, bottle caps and wooden spools, and fashioning a rug from my mother's discarded Evening in Paris powder puff. Of course, wanting a dollhouse as a child was not unusual, but my desire for one may have been intensified because my family moved frequently. By the time I was five years old, we had lived in five different houses. If I'd had a dollhouse, I could have carried a miniature home with me wherever I went. The rooms of the real houses we moved to would change, but the rooms of my dollhouse would stay the same. Maybe the idea of a world I could control appealed to me as an adult, too. I could reach a godlike hand into a small room and rearrange furniture, moving a chair that wasn't much bigger than a Monopoly token.

Unlike my own house where my children left wet towels on the floor and dirty dishes in the sink, a dollhouse would be a miniature world that stayed pristine and perfect. There would be no scuffmarks or crumbs on the dollhouse floors, no muddy sneakers in the doorway, no dirty clothes to wash. I'd given up on getting any help with housekeeping from my husband and children, but maybe a dollhouse would compensate for the lack of order I couldn't maintain in my daily life.

When I turned 45, my husband asked what I wanted for my birthday, and I said, "A dollhouse." He couldn't afford to buy an expensive pre-assembled dollhouse, so we went to a craft store and bought a dollhouse kit. His gift to me would be to assemble the dollhouse. The gift would be extra-special because my husband was going to make it for me.

After he brought the kit home and took it out of the box, he realized that putting the dollhouse together was going to be more complicated than he had thought. There were tiny shingles to glue to the roof, toothpick-sized railings to assemble, fragile plastic "panes" to slide into the window frames. I bought sheets of Thumbelina-sized wallpaper and suggested that we wire the rooms with miniature light fixtures that could be turned on and off.

He did what he usually did when he felt overwhelmed. Instead of working on the dollhouse, he put it back in the box and slid the box under the bed in our guest room. Every so often I would remind him that he still hadn't completed my birthday present, and he would scowl, grumble, or shrug. This went on for several years.

Maybe I could have tried to put the dollhouse together myself, but I was not handy with paint and a glue gun.

When I tried to perform tasks that required such attention to detail and dexterity, my hands trembled and I became frustrated and impatient. My husband on the other hand, was an amateur artist with an eye for detail. Everything he did was meticulous; people sometimes thought his original paintings were created from paint-by-number kits because the lines were so precise. Even when he painted the interior walls of our house, he would use a sable paintbrush on the edges and corners. Anyway, making the dollhouse was supposed to have been his birthday gift to me. Instead, all I had was a box of loose shingles and balsa-wood sticks.

Finally, I confronted him while he was hunched over, silently painting tiny bricks onto a canvas. Why did he have time to paint a picture of a brick storefront but no time to complete the dollhouse he had promised me?

After that, he began working on the dollhouse at the kitchen table. He spent many Saturday afternoons studying the instructions, standing occasionally to appraise the structure from a distance, pleased with its progress. First, he painted the foundation with faux bricks outlined with thin rectangles of gray "mortar." Then, he constructed the first level with an intricate staircase leading to the second story. The exterior had Williamsburg blue clapboards, white gingerbread trim, and red window frames and doors. As weeks passed into months, the second story emerged with its lattice-trimmed balcony and two bedrooms with bay windows. Then, he added the third floor: one room was a nursery with teddy bear wallpaper; the other room was a bathroom. Finally, he completed a tiny attic and began hot-gluing shingles to the turreted roof, topped with a weathervane.

Once the dollhouse was built, the fun started. I couldn't afford to redecorate my real house, but I could enjoy furnishing my toy one. I bought a miniature kitchen stove and sink; a hutch that I filled with diminutive cups, pans and canisters; a wire basket of eggs; and a wooden crate of apples. My sister gave me an elfin tea set purchased on a trip to Japan. My children presented me with dollhouse furniture and accessories for Christmas, Mother's Day, and birthdays: a sofa, chair, and footstool: a TV with rabbit-ears (a peewee version of the one my husband and I had watched when we were newlyweds); a canopy bed and dresser for the master bedroom; a crib, high chair, and itsy-bitsy Pampers™ box for the nursery; and a claw foot bathtub, pedestal sink, toilet, and Mr. Bubble™ box for the bathroom. Scouring antique stores, my friend Susan found a tiny Persian rug that had once been a prize in a cigarette pack and a little Christmas tree that I placed in the living room in December and stored in the attic (along with a tiny treasure chest) the rest of the year. I purchased a thimble-sized sewing machine that looked just like the Singer my mother had stitched my dresses on when I was a child. Using twigs for "logs," my husband fashioned a fireplace for the living room. I bought an anniversary clock that was a miniature replica of the glass-domed one my parents had kept on their mantel when I was growing up, and taped a postage-stamp-sized portrait of a bride and groom above the fireplace. The wedding picture kept falling from the wall because the double-sided masking tape I had used to attach it wasn't strong enough.

Although I pored through catalogs and browsed in hobby shops, I never found a family to live in the house. Victorian dolls dressed in velveteen and lace were out of context with the TV and '50s-era Elvis record album in the living room; modern dolls either were not to scale or were so crudely featured that I couldn't bring myself to buy them. Maybe I resisted finding a family because positioning them in the dollhouse would force me to examine my own family's dysfunction. Would the dollhouse family drink cocoa together in front of the fireplace instead of retreating to the far corners of the house, as my family did? Would the dollhouse couple sleep in the same bed, or would they sleep in separate bedrooms, as my husband and I did? As long as the house remained vacant, I could still project my own fantasies onto its walls.

(Well, in truth, there was one resident: a plastic baby doll with a '60s bubble hairdo. Although the doll was small, she was too big for the house, an oversized Alice in Wonderland among the smaller chairs and beds. I didn't like the doll, but I was stuck with her since my mother-in-law, thinking she would be the ideal addition to my Lilliputian world, had given her to me. So there she sat with a tiny *Highlights* magazine in her lap, a hulking Baby Huey in the nursery, plopped in front of a crib that she was too huge to fit into.)

Seven years after bringing the dollhouse kit home, we celebrated our 25th wedding anniversary, which also was my birthday. We took the train to New Orleans and stayed in a hotel in the French Quarter, but as we sat across the table from each other drinking Hurricanes and eating jambalaya, we had nothing to say to each other. Later, I sat on the hotel bed crying because my husband hadn't given me a birthday present. First, he said the trip to New Orleans was my gift, but after I pointed out that the trip was an anniversary gift for both of us, he suggested that I take the credit card and go buy myself something in the morning.

"I could go max out the credit card on some expensive jewelry," I said, "but that's not the same as getting a gift someone else picked out for me. The whole purpose of a gift is that someone else chooses it."

Eight months later, I asked him for a divorce and handed him a list of items I wanted to take with me. In the margin next to the dollhouse he wrote a single word in black ink: "No!" Of course, he had put many hours into the dollhouse, painting the intricate bricks on the foundation and hearth, but it had been a birthday gift, albeit a belated one. He argued that the dollhouse kit had been the gift, not the finished product, and offered to buy another dollhouse kit that "someone else" could put together. He had reason to be angry—I had fallen in love with another man—but I was surprised that a man who was too self-consciously masculine to wear a pink shirt would so fiercely hang onto a "girlie" dollhouse.

Friends have suggested that maybe he wanted to keep the dollhouse because it represented a "labor of love." That may seem like a plausible explanation, but after I'd spent years begging him to finish it, the dollhouse seemed less like a loving gesture and more like a chore he had grudgingly performed. Did he really want the dollhouse, or did he want to withhold the gift he had given me, to symbolically undo any affection expressed during our marriage?

Finally, in exasperation, I yelled, "Okay, keep the damn dollhouse! But the kids will know you kept something that belongs to me. They know it was my birthday present. They know who it belongs to."

After that, he reluctantly agreed that it was mine.

I swaddled the dollhouse in bubble wrap and moved it in a U-Haul, along with my books, Japanese figurines, blue Danish plates, and a few pieces of furniture, to my new destination in North Carolina. Since I was unemployed, I moved in with my parents until I could find a job, storing the dollhouse in a locker. The man I'd fallen in love with said I could move in with him, but I wanted time to live independently. I didn't want to bounce from one bad marriage into another one.

During those years of single living, I moved the dollhouse four times as I traveled from job to job, town to town, apartment to apartment. After the second move, I started wondering if keeping the dollhouse had been a mistake since it was so fragile to move and difficult to display in the small apartments I rented. Besides, my taste changed when my life became more transient: instead of a romantic style of vintage lace, stained glass, and heirloom roses, my preferences leaned more toward a minimalist style of Zen candles, lucky bamboo, and river rocks. The Victorian dollhouse I had fought so hard to keep had become a burden, a reminder of my failed marriage, my ex-husband's bitterness, and my own infidelity. Even though I carefully shrouded it in bubble wrap the third time I moved, a porch railing came loose and a delicate wooden gutter snapped and had to be mended with glue.

Now I live with my second husband in a log cabin, where the dollhouse is displayed on an antique table in the guest room. It's a curiosity or conversation piece for our guests, but we seldom see it. My new husband isn't interested in dollhouses, especially one my ex-husband made, and I don't need to look at my doll house to know that there is no dwelling, real or imagined, where everything remains in place, spotless and perfect.

Even the dollhouse is flawed. The porch railing is crooked, and—despite the glue—the gutter is cracked like a broken bone that has healed but will never be straight again.

Beth Copeland

JIMMY'S ROOM

Brian Behr Valentine

Ben stood at Jimmy's bedside in his musty-smelling room. Jimmy's tiny body was not more than three feet long; tiny little arms and legs ending in tinier little hands and feet. Conversely, Jimmy's head was enormous, his teeth twice the size of Ben's.

The medical chart read:

November 10th, 10:30 AM
Temperature: Normal.
Urinated: Yes
Bowel: No
Medicine: 5cc Chloral Hydrate Solution
Note: Resting comfortably.

Jimmy did indeed appear to be resting comfortably, and had been for a long time, for he was not among the recently departed. He had baked in the summer and frozen in the winter for almost a century. He was now a tiny freeze-dried mummy.

The house was a huge, three story affair; expanded, wings on wings, over decades without the aid of architectural expertise or common sense. Built as a Midwestern stock-baron's week-end country estate in the eighteen fifties, the family had lost it in the down-turn of the 1890s. The deed revealed it had turned over repeatedly in the intervening century, but no one had lived in the giant dump now for twenty years. Ben wanted his own bed and breakfast and had quit his job and poured his savings into the huge fixer-upper.

While painting upstairs—with the standard entrepreneurial worry of failure on his mind—he decided to remove the ancient full-length mirror from the master bedroom wall. The frame turned out to be a secret door into a small, secret attic compartment.

Oh please, he thought. *Let it be someone's forgotten vault!* But inside he found a makeshift sickroom: bedpan, washtub, and medical supplies. On the bedside chair a coffee cup—its contents long since evaporated—held down a single, dusty file.

In addition to a birth certificate for 1910, there were care records with two sets of handwriting: a woman's tight, well-formed script and a man's heavy, twitchy letters. Inside the file's cover was a reminder to check the bedroom for occupants before leaving Jimmy's room. *The kids almost caught me today,* in the woman's script. Ben looked to the wall and saw the peepholes.

So, Jimmy had died alone, the parents who kept him secret from everyone, including their own family, had never returned from some outing. A fatal accident? Tragedy heaped on tragedy, Ben mused, and worried over it. Had Jimmy a mind? Did he die wondering why they had not returned, or did he pass away oblivious? There was nothing to indicate the quality of the brain in that roomy skull. Was this a dwarf genius of unknown proportion or a crippled, mindless hydrocephalic?

A stack of books on the shelf, revealed Twain, Wistor, Grey, and others of that ilk. But had they been used to while away the time of the attendant, or to entertain Jimmy with exploits he would never participate in? Had that huge cranium been filled with great, imagined adventures, or was the quiet reading simply a soothing voice to the mind of what would have at that time been called a pinhead? There was no evidence of any sort, and Ben sat in the chair to think.

It was quiet in Jimmy's room; still—just as a tomb should be. That would change Ben realized. The police would come and remove the body, news crews accompanying them. The authorities and the press would speculate much, but would find no answers. Some fool would put the photos on the Internet claiming it was an alien mummy.

Ben's bed and breakfast would be booked years ahead due to this publicity. On a clear day you could almost see the city skyline from the front porch, and once everyone in the city knew about his bed and breakfast, well, you can't buy publicity like this, he mused. He could hint the century of turn-over in ownership was due to ghostly activity. He could look right in the cameras that would come, and say he heard strange noises and saw strange things.

From that perspective, Jimmy's exposure assured financial solvency for Ben. It would; however, do nothing for Jimmy, other than make his lot in death as God-awful as his lot in life.

"This place is more yours than mine," Ben whispered to Jimmy. Some secrets were better off kept, he decided, and backed out, resealing the door. Over the years his bed and breakfast was not at all times booked full, but it always had at least one guest, "resting comfortably."

Mary E. Martin

HOUSE

Spring vines squeeze
through the window
in my study, a stubborn
reminder how this structure
invites invasion.
I welcome the tendrils,
curling in attendance
while I sit, write, dream.

Everything in this house
invites re-vision:
in the dark basement
a discarded husk of a water
heater lies belly up while small
drips echo through the bare
cavern, brick wet and still;
the stairs, which are slowly losing
muscle, tremble as I descend
to check on rising water
after rain. Even here
I understand the compromise
this house has made—
while I siphon water
out, silt settles in,
whatever lives outside
lives in as well.

I bless these walls
that sometime need repair
but always remind me
I need no fixed boundaries:
no matter how grand

the appearance, how secure
the home, there is always
room for dismantling.

Rikki Santer

DOMICILE

He who buries a treasure buries himself with it.
—Gaston Bachelard, *The Poetics of Space*

Beneath the covenant of your roofing you betray us. Your rooms and hallways split and tear beneath the thumbs of your duplicity. You have strong-armed us into every broken corner to customize our instructional manual for despair. You have stumped engineers and lawyers with your skirt over your head, your naked footers exposed for everyone to marvel—except the insurance company that wasn't aroused, or aroused just enough to drop us. It began with hope enough. My typed inquiry mailed in harmony with a childless father, his newspaper feature, and a 1960s California ranch seated atop an Ohio ravine. He invited us to visit and my banana bread wooed him. The fresh death of his wife was to move him on to smaller floors but not before he deemed my little family the stewards of the dream house they had built together. Praise the wet bar, the movie set kitchen, the tiki room ready to rocket jump into rumpus. Months later, after he died, we buried his dentures, as he directed, under his wife's pregnant peonies. But today, just a few years in, our herd of pink flamingoes runs plastic through your dying ash trees while you flaunt the demented gaps and fissures of your torqued and tortured spine. We try to imagine that you are a home of cinder blocks filled with magic custard; that we share residence with contortionist doors that know how to untwist the twisted, with walkways that remember ways to deftly clean their teeth. Yet you are a ship sinking, a caboose wobbling, a home wrecker wrecking. You are a frame that houses our nightmare where in the dark we pace your bones or lay in wait listening to the blind breaths of time and the cold, slippery snakes of foreclosure.

Pauletta Hansel

DAY OF THE DEAD

All my past loves come close now,
though their bodies live in faraway houses,
I see them, hands and faces
pressing flat against the window screens,
and I am trying to remember
why I loved them.

This one, a beehive for a heart;
this one who never tried
to see inside the shroud
I'd wrapped around my own;
this one cracked me open,
drank from me like honey comb;
this one, a cliché—
if I could make him love
me more than whiskey or his wife
I would be saved.

Right now the wind is blowing every
thing it can right up against another—
leaves and litter; cloud and sun.
Tree limbs scratch against tall fences;
birds huddle, feathers folded
on the wires that stretch between
the houses up and down the street,
stretch between
the ones I cannot see.

And I am wondering
about the screens and shrouds and fences
in between the living and the dead,
about the wires held taut

between our memories
and the lives we live in houses.
I am sitting on the porch steps
listening for the silence
stretched between the passing cars,
heading home.

CRUSHED SAGE

Ellen E. Keim

I don't walk down Keshia's street very often. Trash covers the ground, and bored-looking teenagers cluster on the dirty stoops and in the grassless front yards. Kids throw rocks at passing cars and once two men attempted to pull a woman into their car when she was out walking. This is not a street where I would let my daughter sell Girl Scout cookies.

And yet that was where Keshia lived. Hers was one of the plainest houses on the block, a single family home with a rusty chain link fence and toys scattered on the front porch and all around the yard. With its lack of shutters, chipped Masonite siding, and a broken down porch, it didn't look very homey. But it had been a home, to Keshia and her younger sister and two brothers as well as a mom and a dad. An intact family in this neighborhood. Imagine.

When I first met Keshia, I didn't know her family situation. I just assumed that because 40 percent of the households in this neighborhood were headed by single mothers, hers was, too. But I found out later on that Keshia's parents were married and both had jobs: She worked the evening shift at Burger King and he worked as a cook at the nearby university.

Keshia showed up at my house the day I moved in. I was lugging the sixth box of books from my car to the house when I heard someone say, "Hey, lady, whatcha doin'?" I turned to see a scrawny little black girl, hair done up in short beaded braids, wearing a simple shorts set and a frown on her face. She looked no more than seven or eight years old.

She and the kids with her, who were all boys and looked even younger, began to interrogate me. "Do you live here now? Is this your house? What's your name? Do you have any kids? What are their names? Are they gonna live here with you?" They were like a horde of bees buzzing around a newly-discovered flower and they were zeroing in for the bounty.

"Can we help, huh? We'll help you for a dollar. One for each of us. Okay? "

"I don't have a dollar." I said. "And I don't need any help."

"We'll take a quarter. Do you have any quarters?"

I finally relented. "All right. I have a little change. But no dollars. And don't come back here tomorrow asking for more money."

But of course they did. Keshia collected the money and supervised the boys while they did the small chores I manufactured for them. When they offered to help plant my garden, I was hesitant, but decided to give them a chance. After they demolished my third petunia, I chased them off and told them not to come back.

My next-door neighbor had a completely different philosophy. He had little kids hanging around his yard constantly, talking with him as he sat on his front porch, swinging on his hammock, running into his house for a glass of water. I found out later that he was good friends with Keshia's family, that he wasn't just the "Saint of Seventh Avenue." All the little kids—there were really only two of them—were Keshia's little brothers. I had thought of her as their ringleader, but she was actually their babysitter. She kept them in line. When she said it was time to leave, they disappeared, no questions asked.

The elementary school across the street ensured that there would be plenty of kids around. But when the realtor first took me to see the house, it was a quiet weekend and it didn't dawn on me what the school would mean: school buses and lots of children. That ten times a day a recorded male voice would intone: "Please move away from the school bus. The school bus is about to move." That the kids waiting for the buses would wake me every school day morning with their shrill voices. That they would pick on each other mercilessly, tear limbs off trees, destroy the lawn of the lady's house next door, and climb on fences and wiggle them until they came loose. And that I would be afraid to yell at them for fear of what they might do to me or my property.

The neighborhood I moved into was what some people call "in transition" and others call "marginal." That meant it was still undesirable, but at least it wasn't stagnant or declining. The elementary school was new and the Section 8 housing was being revamped, but only 14 percent of the homes were owner-occupied and at least a fifth of them were papered with bright orange "Vacant" notices. Income levels averaged $15,000 for homeowners and $5,000 for those in the ubiquitous government housing. (Almost half of the city's Section 8 apartments were located there.) 41 percent of all households had no access to vehicles and 15 percent didn't have a phone.

And yet something about the neighborhood appealed to me. All my life I'd lived in the suburbs, where everyone is alike. I thought I would like being lost in a sea of diversity; that it would confer a freedom to be myself that I'd never felt in suburbia. I also liked the feeling of being at the center of the city: all the major freeways, hospitals, theaters, museums, and several colleges and universities were only minutes away. Best of all, I didn't even need a car—everything I needed was within walking distance.

I completely forgot that I had once driven through this neighborhood with held breath, certain that I was going to be a victim of a drive-by shooting. I only vaguely remembered that a notorious gang called the Short North Posse had terrorized the neighborhood for years (until most of its members were rounded up and sent to prison). I didn't know and didn't care that the crime rate in this area was almost twice what it was for the city as a whole. I didn't really think of any of that when I turned to the realtor and said, "I want to make an offer."

When I first saw this house in its bucolic setting, shootings and muggings were the furthest thing from my mind. Light gray with white trim, it was situated at the top of a hill on a (then) quiet street lined with huge maple, sycamore and catalpa trees. Although the yard was tiny, it was neatly landscaped with hostas and daylilies, a huge climbing white rose bush and well-trimmed yews around the front porch. Inside, the house looked like a package of cream mints: all pastel colors and white woodwork. As soon as I set foot in it I felt at home.

My house was one of what I liked to call "The Three Sisters." They were built in 1915 on adjoining lots owned by a woman named Mary Dickinson; she built them to get a break on her taxes. Although minor changes had been made over the years, the bones of each house were still the same: a steep four-gabled roof with a "tower" (really a two-story bay) built onto one side, with one bathroom, three bedrooms (large, medium and tiny as if they were for the three bears), a curving staircase with an octagon window lighting the landing, a front room with a corner fireplace, a middle room with the bay and a kitchen across the back. Like a lot of old houses, there was a large archway between the front and middle "parlors." The overall effect was what Germans call gemütlich.

Three days after I moved in, I looked out the kitchen window and saw a boy running down the street shooting a gun into the air. The following week a neighbor had a window shot out in her car. Another neighbor's car was punctured with bullet holes, as were all the stop signs. I learned to differentiate between shots and fireworks (and that gunshots were sometimes used in lieu of fireworks). Helicopters with searchlights often circled right over my house and once I heard someone shouting through a bullhorn, "We know you're in there. Come out with your hands up."

Even after the area improved (judging by fewer incidents of gunfire and helicopters) five of the 12 houses on my street alone still stood vacant. Looters stripped the house next door of its downspouts and the copper tubing in the air conditioning unit. My other neighbor's house was broken into twice in one summer. A garage at the end of the alley was burned to the ground.

But learning to live in a high-crime area wasn't my greatest challenge. The most disconcerting part of living in the neighborhood was my reaction to its residents. I discovered I was a snob, even though I had no grounds to be. After all, I lived in an urban neighborhood not because I had the money to invest in rehabbing a house—I lived here because, like most of the other residents, it was all I could afford. I might have been raised in an upper-middle-class neighborhood, but those days were long gone for me.

But my snobbery wasn't limited to socio-economic status. I also found out that I was prejudiced. It took me a long time to get used to being one of the few whites in the neighborhood. I got anxious every time I saw a black man coming toward me when I was out walking.

At first I said hi to everyone I met on the street. Even to the tough-looking young men with scowls on their faces. I was surprised at the number of responses I got, but not as surprised as they seemed to be that I greeted them in the first place. Eventually, though, I learned to keep to myself. I finally figured out that people mistrusted my motives. (Is she going to ask for money/try to convert me?) It seemed more prudent to keep my eyes downcast as I passed someone. I got very good at it.

But then something else began to happen: strangers spoke to me when I was working in my yard. I had always thought of gardening as a solitary activity, but instead it turned out to be my garden that connected me to other people. Young, old, black, white, male, female; I was gratified by the number of people who complimented me on my garden as they walked by. (And there was always someone walking by; my house was located on a main route to the bus stop, the neighborhood grocery store, the liquor store and the library.)

Working with the soil and watching things grow had helped me work through my grief when my parents had died years before, but it had been a long time since I'd had a garden of my own. Because the hill my house stood on was scantily covered with grass, and prone to become an army of shoulder-high weeds—and because I didn't have a lawn mower—I decided that my first project would be to dig up the entire slope and try to start a terraced garden. I planted ivy (I'd brought some with me from my old house), White Nancy, two kinds of sedum, bishop's weed, pineapple mint, and hens and chicks—all plants that were given to me or discreetly filched from other people's gardens. Then I accented the green and white foliage with transplanted daylilies.

An ancient maple in front of the house made that area too shady for sun-loving plants. One of the few sunny spots was a 1' by 4' plot along the side of our front porch. I decided that would be an ideal place for an herb garden. I planted basil, rosemary, oregano, cilantro and sage and did my best to keep them alive and thriving.

I was watering them one day when I looked up and saw Keshia and another little girl leaning on my fence. Her friend, all smiles and dimples, introduced herself and spelled her name for me: Shaquila.

Then Keshia asked, "Whatcha doin'?"

"I'm watering my herb garden."

"What's a *erb* garden?"

"You use herbs when you cook things. They each have a different taste and smell." I broke off little pieces from each plant and crushed them between my fingers and let them smell the resulting odors. Their eyes grew round. They asked more questions: What did they taste like? What were they called? I answered all their questions, happy to be talking about my little garden. The girls were quiet for a minute and then Keshia said, "You really love those plants, don't you?"

I was speechless. At that moment all I could think of was how I'd chased her and her brothers away from my garden. I'd seen Keshia as just another of those pesky kids and completely missed the fact that she was a person capable of the sensitivity it takes to recognize what another person cherishes. It wasn't just that she appreciated my gardening efforts. It was about her understanding me. And because she asked the question, I was better able to understand her.

I felt so ashamed. I was spending hours every day planting my perennials and watering and weeding while my next-door neighbor did the same except with kids. I could pour out all my love and energy on a plant in the dirt, but I didn't want to be bothered with people. I thought of the belief some gardeners have that you should talk to plants because they have feelings. And it struck me: If that's true of plants, wouldn't it be even truer of children?

I'd like to say that my mind was turned around that day so that I immediately began to open up to the neighborhood kids, but it wasn't; maybe I was too set in my ways. Besides, the damage had already been done. For the most part the kids knew to stay away and except for that one conversation I had with Keshia and Shaquila I didn't talk to any of them.

Two years after I first met her, on April 4, 2000, a fire broke out in Keshia's house. Her mom had just come home from work and was chatting with a neighbor when she saw smoke and flames coming from her house. The 911 call came into the nearby fire station at 11:50 p.m. and the first fire truck was there in two minutes. It took four minutes to bring out the family. Keshia was found on the stair landing and her 7-year-old brother, Gary, Jr. was found in an upstairs bedroom. The three-year-old twins, Michelle and Michael, were downstairs; their father was found at the door to their room. It was later determined that the fire was caused by one of the many extension cords the family had been using because there weren't enough outlets.

Michelle died within hours; Keshia died the following day. Their father was burned so badly he had to have his arms amputated; he died two months later. Michael and Gary, Jr. were the only ones to survive.

I hadn't even known about the fire. I must have slept right through the clamor of the sirens. It wasn't until I was reading a weekly paper on my lunch break a few days later that I saw the picture of Keshia. "My God, I know her! She lives right around the corner from me." My brain was slow to catch up on the reason why her picture was in the paper.

I was surprised to learn that Keshia had been 12 and in the fifth grade. Her teacher described her as loving, helpful and giving. "She was really caring about her little brothers and sister." That was also when I found out that she lived with her mother and father and that her parents were married and employed. I wasn't surprised about the fire: house fires are common enough especially in cold weather and in the derelict houses that some people are forced to call home. But I'd never known anyone before who had died in one.

That it was Keshia struck me as the ultimate irony: I had dismissed her once and if she hadn't died I may have never thought about her again. Now I would never be able to forget her.

Last night I dreamed that she was grown up, something she will never be, and smiling, something I never saw her do. She haunts me all out of proportion as to how well I knew her.

After the fire, after the house had been torn down and nothing was left but a tiny city lot (it was hard to believe that a house had ever stood there), I fantasized about putting in a memorial garden—a grief garden, if you will—for Keshia and her family. But I never did. Instead, the lot stands as a memorial of its own, empty as it is, with no sign of any one ever having lived there.

It's been thirteen years since Keshia died. I still live in my little house on my tiny lot. I sit on my front porch and watch the young women pushing their babies in strollers. If Keshia had lived she would have probably been one of them. I bet she would have been a good mother.

Whenever I work in my garden, I think of her. I remember her softly saying, "You really love those plants, don't you?" If she hadn't asked me that question I might not ever have realized how much my garden does mean to me. And if she hadn't died, I would never have realized how much a person—any person—can matter.

Ellen E. Klein

William Derge

THEIR ROOM

It was like an arctic region,
the last to be explored,
a square, bright quarter,
rounded in the imperfection of vision.
In the center, the queen-sized bed,
floating regally over the blue shag carpet,
left little new land to discover.
But, taboo made up for lack of terrain,
though, my mother was to confess later,
not a single one of us was conceived there,
nor, I think, ever could have been.
The eyes of the virgin and all the saints
were like cold, blue stars crowning a pole,
and one entire sun-bleached wall,
held our first communion pictures,
all of us dipped in white,
the girls in see-through bridal veils,
mother of pearl rosaries draped just so
over the thumbs meaty crotch,
our faces pale with innocence,
fresh from the steamy dark confessional.

Which left the closet to explore.

You approached it reverentially,
stocking feet gliding over the glazed floor.
The door knob was porcelain white,
round and shiny like my father's head.
Inside, before the blackness, hung his ties,
thick as hairs, that moved
in a single wave when you opened the door.

Ignorant of fashion's changes,
we never questioned why he had so many,
since he only wore them for weddings, funerals,
and those rare dates with my mother.
They were of all widths and designs:
the wide thirties and forties, the narrow fifties,
the crazy paisley sixties, the cool seventies,
the monotonous eighties, where they end.
There was a hand-painted Hula dancer, champagne
glasses and bubbles on a harvest-gold field,
Mondrian rectangles, Jackson Pollack squiggles,
a whole scene where a trout leapt out of a mountain stream,
a sunset over the Grand Canyon,
the Lovers' leap at the Dells,
lightning bolts, cold, blue ribbons of fire.

And then, suddenly, the darkness of the cave.
Slowly, you parted the hanging shirts and pant legs,
feeling the heat escape, to find the silk,
maroon smoking jacket, arms folded, on the shelf,
or, at Christmas, the presents, already wrapped,
mercilessly out of reach.
But mostly, there were the baker's uniforms,
white, starched, and folded, or, white with dough,
thrown rumpled on the floor,
the white baker's hats, flat and wrinkled,
deflated balloons.

William Derge

OUR HOUSE

Christine Eskilson

Jack looked so happy standing in the empty dining room that Julia couldn't help but feel guilty about the nub of fear in her stomach. But it was there. It had started as a twinge at the first open house, blossomed into a dull ache when Jack kept dragging her back to see the place, and finally took up residence just below her ribcage at the closing. For all intents and purposes the fear appeared permanent. At least until this latest passion faded and Jack began agitating for a dry cleaners within walking distance and an extra-large coffee mocha.

"Jules, come over here and picture this." Jack pushed open the French doors leading out to the redwood deck. Nestled in the green meadow, just beyond the deck, was a small outbuilding that Jack had already announced would be barn red before the first snowfall. "We'll have our coffee and paper out here and then I'll kiss you good-bye and voila! A few short steps and I'm thrashing away. It's perfect."

Julia joined him outside. "And I'll get in the car, drive twelve minutes to the commuter rail and still have another forty-five minutes before I'm at the office," she noted dryly.

Jack clasped her hands and searched her face with the green eyes she never tired of looking at. "Jules, you're not getting second thoughts, are you? It's a big sacrifice for you, the commute and all, but I thought you wanted this too. I thought we agreed that we needed to get out of the city, be on our own." Jack stroked her fingers with his thumb. "If either of us hates it we'll move back to Boston. Right away."

"I know that, Jack. I agreed to try living out here. The train won't be that bad—I can catch up on my reading." She gave a little laugh. "I always wanted to tackle *War and Peace*."

He didn't even crack a smile. "Is it the other thing then?" he asked, his voice softer. "Are you still thinking about her?" Along with Jack's renewed commitment to their marriage, six months of counseling had produced an agreement not to utter the name of one of their former neighbors.

"No, it's not that."

"Good," Jack said. "Believe me, I want to make sure you never think about her again."

I don't, Julia thought, I'm far too terrified about something else.

As they stood together in the twilight, Julia realized that this was the perfect time—the perfect time to say, Jack, dear, you know I couldn't stand to live with you in the same brownstone as that blonde bitch any longer but when I said yes to this house I must have been temporarily out of my mind. I know you need space for your painting—I know you now fancy yourself a gentleman organic farmer, but I just can't possibly live here. Not in this house.

Julia took a deep breath. "Jack," she began, "about this house..."

"It's the kitchen, isn't it?" he rushed in, eager to please. "You loved the hardwood floors we had on Marlborough Street. I don't mind terra cotta tile but we can rip it up and put down pine. Anything you want. All I want is for you to be happy."

"That would be fine," Julia said weakly. A deal was a deal, she reminded herself.

But the nub lingered.

Jack gave her a big hug, massaging her back with his knuckles. "It's going to work out, honey, I know it will. This is the house for us—for us and our kids," he murmured into her hair. "Don't think about what happened in Boston. It's all behind us."

He was so damned obtuse that Julia finally gave into the fear nestled in her belly. "But what about what happened here?" she whispered back.

Jack pulled away from her and shook his head. "We've gone over this, Julia. I thought it was already settled." His tone was noticeably chillier. "Isn't it a little late to bring it up all over again now—on our first night?"

"I know we did, but I'm still having a hard time with it."

"It didn't happen to us," Jack said, shrugging his shoulders, "it's not our history." He sounded so sure of himself, Julia thought.

But it was the history of the house and they had known this history when they closed the deal. Sondra, their cheery real estate agent, had told them and it was there by law in tiny print on the listing sheet. It was also reflected in the price, which meant a lot considering Jack hadn't sold a big painting in nearly a year and Julia still was only a junior partner. This beautiful house—Jack's dream "updated Victorian farmhouse" in real estate parlance—was the Warren house. The house where three years before Leo Warren had stabbed his wife with a carving knife late one night and fled in the family Suburban with two sleeping children. He'd driven deep into the woods to a deserted lake. There, he left the car in gear and pushed his young son and daughter, carefully strapped into their car seats, into the murky water. As the lake lapped over the windshield, Leo blew his brains out.

That model of fatherhood made Jack's drunken fling with infidelity look like forgetting to take out the garbage.

Although Julia grieved for the mother, she tried most not to think about the children. She'd seen Jack's nephews conk out reliably on car trips and she fervently hoped the Warren kids had never woken up. As for Leo, Julia had always wondered why he hadn't just shot himself in the first place, before rummaging through the kitchen knives.

The Warren triple murder-suicide predictably had gotten huge play in the Boston press. It was one of those stories that gripped Julia for a few days and then receded into the stack of newspapers she kept for recycling by the kitchen door. Now she might be living it all over again, every single day.

Julia let Jack lead her back into the house. "If either of us hates it, we can move, right, Jack?" she said, forcing herself to sound light.

"In the wink of an eye, my sweet," he agreed. "Now," he said, gazing at the unhung pictures stacked beside the dining room fireplace, "where can we get some decent takeout in these bucolic rolling hills?"

Julia smiled in spite of herself. It reminded her of college when Jack, after working in the studio most of the night while she'd studied for an econ exam, would crawl into her narrow bed with figs and prosciutto or some other nocturnal delicacy. "You should have thought of that before we left Back Bay."

As Jack unearthed the thin telephone book that was the sum and substance of their new community, the doorbell rang. "Who could that be?" Jack asked, raising an eyebrow at Julia. "Our lovely Sondra, perhaps, nosing around for a further commission? I'd give her an extra percentage for a double order of shrimp pad Thai."

Julia shook her head as she maneuvered her way around moving cartons to the front door. Maybe they'd be back in the city sooner than she thought.

It wasn't their real estate agent, nor was it an order of Pad Thai, but Jack wasn't that far off. The gray-haired woman on the front steps carried a glass-topped casserole dish that almost landed at Julia's feet when she opened the door.

"Oh, I'm so sorry," the woman stammered as she fumbled to maintain a grip on the Corning ware. After she recovered herself, she held out a large, firm hand. "Are you Mrs. Barnes?" the woman asked, "I'm Mrs. Strong, Esther Strong, from the brick house next door. Welcome to Fairhaven Lane."

The casserole didn't look particularly appetizing but it appeared hot and relatively intact. Julia bit back her traditional response—"There is no Mrs. Barnes, my name is Julia Knowles"—and nodded her head.

"I'm afraid things are a little chaotic," Julia said, gesturing at the boxes piled behind her in the foyer, "we haven't really started to unpack yet." Then, afraid she had sounded ungracious, she hastily added, "Would you like to come in?"

Mrs. Strong's polite demurral was interrupted by Jack's appearance, telephone book still in hand.

"Esther, is that you? I'm so glad you came over." He reached out and relieved her of the dish. "This looks wonderful," he declared, "You'll have to stay and help us inaugurate the dining room." Mrs. Strong smiled for the first time and Julia thought, Jack always has a way with older women. The younger ones, too, for that matter.

Mrs. Strong's offering turned out to be tastier than Julia had anticipated. The three of them had a pleasant enough evening, balancing paper plates while perched on boxes of unpacked books. The furniture was due to arrive from Marlborough Street tomorrow. Jack built a fire and dug up a bottle of wine, managing to get the cork out with a coat hanger. Mrs. Strong was reserved at first, but then her face grew rosy and, egged on by Jack, she expounded on the virtues of their new home. She told Jack the nearest place to pick up the Sunday Times and advised Julia on the best hair dresser in the county. "In case you're thinking of a change, my dear," she said, staring at Julia's shoulder-length curly brown hair, "Marianne's a wonder with the shorter hairstyles."

It could have been the wine but as Julia closed the door on their new neighbor a warm glow spread through her body. She ran her hand over the beaded wainscoting in the foyer. Maybe Jack's right, she thought, this is a lovely house and we'll create our own memories. It's nice to have a friendly next door neighbor bringing over ham and scalloped potatoes, and dispensing beauty tips. She felt Jack's eyes upon her and turned to him with a smile. "I liked our Mrs. Strong," she announced, "although I'm not ready to give up my cuts on Newbury Street."

"I like your hair the way it is," Jack said, leaning against the carved post at the base of the stairs, "Esther's a trip, isn't she? Once she gets going she manages to have an opinion on everything."

"You've obviously met her before. Why didn't you tell me?"

Jack hesitated. "I met her when I came out here to figure out the studio layout."

"But why didn't you tell me?" Julia persisted.

Jack folded his lean body onto the stairs, his blue jean clad legs stretched out in front of him. "Jules, you're bound to find out sooner or later, but the truth is she's Leo's older sister."

"Leo's sister?" Julia repeated. Then, as the connection dawned, "you mean Leo Warren?" The glow was replaced by a sudden chill.

"I didn't want to tell you until you had a chance to meet her and see that she's a perfectly nice woman. I know this thing with Leo has you a little spooked."

"It's not 'a thing with Leo'," Julia corrected sharply. "A guy living in this very house slaughtered his entire family and now you tell me his sister is still hovering next door."

Jack threw up his hands. "And I'm sure it's awful for her as well, Jules. In fact she told me she couldn't leave. She doesn't own her place. Her husband left it in some sort of trust to a charity but she can live in it until she dies. She can't afford to go anywhere else."

Julia reconsidered. "You're right, it probably is awful for her—the whole town knows her brother was a psychotic nutcase. I'm sure there's whispering and pointing that she'll never get away from."

"And she does make a mean casserole," Jack pointed out.

"Okay, she can stay," Julia decided with a heavy mock sigh, "but I don't have to be best friends with her, right?"

Jack held out his arms. "Your best friend is right here."

As Julia started toward him, Jack slapped the side of his head. "Damn, Jules, but I've got some work to do. I promised Damien I'd get him some sketches on the Danbury Park mural by tomorrow." He looked at her sheepishly. "Can we pretend tomorrow is our first night all over again?"

"That we can," Julia promised, "and I'll bring the Pad Thai."

The Sunday following their dinner with Mrs. Strong Julia was dozing in the bright Indian summer sunshine on the deck. She and Jack had made significant headway sorting out boxes and arranging furniture. Jack permitted Julia to put her battered barrister's bookcase in the living room and she let him pick out the rug for the study. Julia had survived two roundtrips into Boston and, although she hadn't yet taken up Tolstoy or Dickens, she found that the train ride relaxed her and gave her precious time to read the newspaper.

"Hello, anyone home?" a voice called out from the flagstone path that ran alongside the house.

Julia's eyes fluttered open and she sat up in her white wicker chair. "I'm up here," she answered, "who's there?"

She heard heavy footsteps on the outside stairs that led up to the deck and Mrs. Strong materialized, carrying a mesh bag. This woman must never travel empty-handed, Julia thought, biting back a smile.

"It's just me," Mrs. Strong announced. "Jack mentioned that you were planning a garden and I had some extra crocus bulbs left over from my fall planting. I thought you might like them."

"Thank you, thank you very much," Julia said, squinting into the sunlight. "Jack's actually the gardener in the family. In fact, he's out shopping for a roto-something or other right now. It's one of the reasons we left Boston."

"You work down there, don't you?" Mrs. Strong asked. "Jack said you're a lawyer."

"A lawyer who sometimes works much to hard," Julia confessed with a sigh. "I should have gone into the office today but it's just too beautiful to be shut inside." She rose from her chair and took the bulbs from Mrs. Strong. "You'll have to excuse my ignorance but do you have any recommendations about where these should go?"

"Oh, you don't have to worry about crocuses. They'll come up anywhere. They're blue—they'll go nice with your eyes." Mrs. Strong pursed her lips. "The side path might make the most impact, but Jack'll probably have his own ideas."

"Side path," Julia repeated. "I'll remember that."

"It's funny, but Elizabeth was never much of a gardener," Mrs. Strong suddenly remarked, brushing her hands on her kelly green corduroy skirt, "there's a wonderful plot of full sunlight right by the back fence but she couldn't even get a dandelion to grow there. I tried to help her time and again but nothing seemed to thrive in her hands."

"Elizabeth was Leo's—your brother's wife?" Julia asked carefully.

Mrs. Strong nodded. "I figured Jack would have told you by now."

"Yes, he did." Mrs. Strong waited, as if she expected Julia to continue, and she grasped for the right words. "I—I really don't know what to say. I remember hearing about it when it happened. It's a horrible story."

"It was and it is," said Mrs. Strong briskly. "Especially since Leo was innocent. No one believes me, of course, but he was."

Now Julia was truly at a loss. "I didn't realize there was any question about—about what happened."

Mrs. Strong waved her hands. "Oh, dear, I misspoke. I don't mean he didn't do it. What I mean is that there must have been some reason. Something or more likely someone must have driven him to it. You're a lawyer, people get driven to the edge all the time, do things they don't really want to do, isn't that right?"

They usually call those people criminally insane, Julia thought but didn't say. "I don't practice that kind of law, Mrs. Strong," Julia replied. "I do municipal bond work, I don't know much at all about criminal law."

"I suppose not," said Mrs. Strong. She put her hand on the railing of the deck stairs. "Well, I'm sorry to have disturbed your day. Enjoy this weather." Her shoulders bowed slightly, Mrs. Strong descended onto the first step.

"You don't have to run off like that," Julia said, not quite sure why she was saying it. "I may not be an expert on crocus bulbs but I can brew a great cup of coffee. Can I offer you one?"

Mrs. Strong flashed a shy smile as she returned to the deck. "I'd like that very much."

She must be terribly lonely, Julia realized as she brought out a tray with two mugs of coffee and a plate of almond cookies from Jack's favorite Back Bay bakery. It's not going to kill me to share a half-hour of my Sunday with her.

Julia's projected thirty minutes turned into closer to an hour as Mrs. Strong launched into the intricacies of canning pickled cucumbers and peach jam. Their next-door neighbor apparently was a devoted cook, as well as a crackerjack gardener. "I hope you liked the casserole," Mrs. Strong said, "I don't think it actually turned out to be one of my better efforts."

"It was delicious," Julia assured her.

"I almost dropped it on your front steps the night we met," Mrs. Strong went on, "you reminded me so much of someone I used to know."

“I hope that’s a compliment,” Julia said with a smile.

Mrs. Strong didn’t answer directly. “And for some reason I expected you to have long blonde hair."

"Why did you think that?"

"All the times I saw Jack here a blonde woman was waiting in the car.” Mrs. Strong’s giggle sounded sly to Julia. “I assumed she was his wife but he never introduced us. Then when you opened the door, I got all mixed up."

"That must have been Sondra, our real estate agent. She's a blonde," Julia said, a little stiffly.

"Sondra Haywood? Oh yes, I've heard of her but I've never actually met her. Of course that's who it was. Sondra Haywood. She must have blonde hair, her mother certainly did."

After Mrs. Strong left Julia stuffed the bag of crocus bulbs in the bottom of the garbage can.

That night at dinner Julia told Jack about Mrs. Strong's version of her brother's crimes. "It was pathetic, really. She seemed to want so desperately to blame someone or something else."

"Hmm," said Jack, finishing his forkful of chicken stir-fry. "I guess it's not that strange for her to think that way. It's hard to believe that someone we care about could have a dark side."

"But sometimes it's staring you right in the face," Julia said. She was only thinking about Mrs. Strong but the sudden flush in Jack's cheeks evoked a memory she had fought to forget: walking in on Jack and their downstairs neighbor in the dimly lit bedroom, clothes strewn on the carpet.

"Do you think Sondra Haywood's pretty?" Julia asked abruptly.

"Whoa, Jules, where's that coming from?"

Julia shrugged. "Mrs. Strong, dark sides, blondes, you name it. Just answer the question."

"Sure, she's attractive. What of it?"

Julia hated the words that came out of her mouth next. "Mrs. Strong told me that she saw you and Sondra together a lot."

Jack's confusion turned to annoyance. "Come on, Jules, Sondra was our real estate agent! Before we closed I couldn't get into the place without her. You were always too busy at the office to come see the house." He pushed back from the table. "I thought we worked really hard to get past that stuff, Julia. I made a mistake once and hurt you very badly, but it can't haunt us for the rest of our lives."

Jack stood up. "I've got work to do. Don't bother waiting up." Julia heard the door to the deck open and close as he headed out to his studio. She was fast asleep long before he returned.

The next morning Jack and Julia were elaborately polite to each other. Neither of them mentioned the night before.

A week later Julia found the crocus bulbs. She had gotten up early for a pre-work stint on the treadmill. She and Jack had set up the treadmill, along with a rack of hand weights, in one of the two smaller bedrooms. They called it the Room of Good Intentions. Before they moved in they'd painted all the bedrooms. Julia had made it a point not to ask which one had belonged to the Warren kids.

The bulbs were scattered randomly around the machine. There was nothing sinister about the small white balls, but their very presence made Julia drop her towel and scream. "Jack!"

He was in the room instantly, his hair still tousled from sleep. "What's wrong?"

She pointed a finger. "It's the crocus bulbs Mrs. Strong brought over. What are they doing here?"

Jack crossed the room and squatted beside the treadmill. "Not getting ready for spring, that's for sure." He flashed her a grin. "You're not exactly a green thumb, honey, but this is ridiculous."

"It's not me. I've never seen these up here before."

Jack retrieved the mesh bag from the corner of the room and began collecting the bulbs. "You said Mrs. Strong brought these over?"

"Yes," Julia said impatiently, "it was last Sunday. You were out searching for the nearest Home Depot. She brought them over and we had coffee and—" She stopped short, not sure how to continue. She didn't want to invite a repeat of the other night's discussion.

Jack picked up the last of the bulbs. "So where did you see these beauties last?"

Julia hesitated. "In the garbage can."

"In the what?"

I put them in one of the garbage cans outside."

"What?" His back was still to her. "Why on earth did you do that?"

"Jack, I don't want to go into it. She said something that touched a nerve and after she left I didn't want to keep them. I can't really explain why."

Jack turned around, twisting the mesh bag in his fingers. "Okay, the nice lonely woman next door brings over bulbs for our garden and you decide to trash them. If that's what you want, I guess I can live with that. But you're sure you didn't dig them out again and leave them here?"

"Yes, I'm sure."

"So if you didn't bring the bulbs upstairs, who did?"

"I don't know, maybe she did," Julia replied sulkily. "Maybe she saw me throw them away and got mad. Leo was her brother, she must know this house inside and out. Maybe she still has a key or maybe she knows a secret way in."

Jack ran one hand through his hair and sighed. "I'll talk to Esther today and try to get to the bottom of this."

When Julia got home from work that evening Jack was on the front porch smoking. She hadn't seen him with a cigarette in years. "What happened with Mrs. Strong?" she asked and plopped her briefcase next to the front door.

He looked at her with an expression she'd never seen before. It was almost as if after knowing her for almost fifteen years and being married for five he was seeing her for the first time. "Esther didn't know what I was talking about," he said slowly. "She assumed you'd planted the bulbs along the side path, like she suggested. I made up some crazy story about why you tossed them—I told her you'd gotten confused—thought they were compost or something."

Julia's heart jumped a beat. "Well, someone put them up in that room."

"I know," Jack said, taking another drag of his cigarette, "but apparently it wasn't Esther. Jules, I'm not very hungry tonight. I've got stuff to do and I'll bring a sandwich out to the studio if you don't mind."

"But what are we going to do about the crocus bulbs?"

"Plant 'em?" Jack asked with a short laugh and then his tone grew serious again. "I don't really know what we can do, Julia."

It was then that she realized he didn't believe her.

After Jack, without comment, agreed to change the lock on the front door, the next few weeks passed in a blur. Julia was working on a big offering at the office and Jack was spending more and more time in the studio, "cranking out the Danbury Park mural," he claimed. Julia saw him only in morning snatches when he'd sleepily open one eye while she buttoned her suit jacket. "Have a good day, Jules," he'd groan and roll over, hugging the pillow to his chest.

Julia never saw Mrs. Strong although sometimes she'd spot fluttering muslin curtains and kitchen lights next door when she pulled out of the driveway in the early morning. There were no more offerings of food or other tokens.

Nothing quite as startling as the appearance of the crocus bulbs occurred, but Julia started to notice other little things out of kilter around the house. One day it was the photo of her grandparents on their fiftieth wedding anniversary; Julia found the silver frame face down on the dining room mantle where it usually stood. Another day it was the books in the study bookcase; Julia distinctly recalled putting them in alphabetical order but discovered Edith Wharton next to Henry James. A pair of socks turned up in her jewelry box and someone left two pints of Ben and Jerry's Cherry Garcia to melt on the kitchen counter.

When she asked Jack about the little oddities on the rare occasions they were both awake at the same time, he denied any knowledge. His ire was only really aroused by the ice cream puddles. "You're sure you didn't take them out to soften just a little and then forgot?" he asked.

"Of course not," she replied, but then again maybe she wasn't so sure. She'd eaten ice cream standing at the kitchen sink after taking a town car home from the office one night at one in the morning. She could have left it out then. The picture in the dining room could have fallen down, and Edith Wharton and Henry James were contemporaries.

She could have accidentally arranged them in order of friendship. And the socks? She was so tired after spending hours at the office that sometimes she didn't know which end was up.

Maybe exhaustion was why it took a few moments for Julia to register what was laid out on the kitchen table when she arrived home the day before Thanksgiving. Because of the holiday, she was able to escape the office in the early afternoon and planned to surprise Jack. She'd picked up a nice bottle of Syrah on the drive from the train. They'd both been so stressed out lately they needed some time to relax.

She flung her coat over the banister and called out his name. No answer. She walked to the back of the house. It was quiet and the kitchen was devoid of signs of life, save the half empty pot of coffee left over from Jack's morning. On the round oak table was a yellowing newspaper. It was a local paper, not the *Globe* or the *Times* that they usually got, and she wondered where Jack had found it. Then she read the headline: *Slain Mom's Two Kids Missing*.

Julia blinked and her chest tightened when she saw that the paper was over three years old. She dropped the bottle of Syrah and ran through the dining room out to the deck, down the stairs and across the meadow to the studio, all the while screaming Jack's name.

The studio was locked. Julia pounded on the door and pulled at the handle, but there was no answer. Where was he?

The tightness in her chest increased and moving on automatic pilot, she turned back toward the house, stumbling blindly through the leaves Jack had promised to rake up last week.

"Julia, are you all right?"

Julia saw Mrs. Strong standing in the line of trees that separated their properties.

"I was in my yard and I heard screaming. Can I help you?" she asked. In the distance Mrs. Strong's pale face looked distorted, as if she was smiling broadly at Julia's torment.

Julia put up one hand. "No, no, I'll be all right." She just wanted to get as far away as she could. But her car keys were in her coat pocket and her coat was in the front hall. When Julia reached the steps to the deck a gust of wind whipped through a pile of leaves and cut through her silk blouse. On the first step she tripped and fell forward, banging her knee on the edge. She winced in pain.

Julia heard breathing behind her and it was Mrs. Strong, firmly helping her to her feet. Mrs. Strong wasn't smiling; her brown eyes were alight with concern. "Julia, please, at least let me help you into the house."

"I need my car keys," Julia mumbled but she let Mrs. Strong take her arm and guide her through the dining room and back into the kitchen. Julia shut her eyes when they entered the room, afraid to see again what lay on the table.

"I think you need to sit down. Can I make you some tea?" Julia heard Mrs. Strong ask and she opened her eyes. The table was empty. Julia stared at the smooth wood. No newspaper. With a sharp cry, Julia collapsed into a chair.

"English Breakfast would be best," Mrs. Strong announced, "there's nothing like a cup of tea to keep your mind off things." Without hesitation she opened the cupboard above the sink and pulled out the box.

Julia still stared at the empty table. Had she only imagined the paper? And where was Jack? She heard Mrs. Strong put a kettle of water on the stove and exclaim, "My goodness!" when she spied the broken wine bottle on the floor.

Mrs. Strong cleaned up the mess and then set down a cup of hot tea in front of Julia. She took a seat beside her.

"So, where did you end up putting the crocus bulbs?" Mrs. Strong asked brightly.

Julia had taken her first sip but with Mrs. Strong's question the tea turned to ice water in her mouth. Her hands began to shake and she put down her cup.

"Julia, what's wrong?"

"Jack," she managed to spit out, "didn't Jack talk to you about the bulbs?"

"Oh no, dear. I haven't spoken to your handsome husband in weeks. I've seen you leave at those crazy hours and he always seems to be in his studio."

In his studio. The studio he'd locked her out of, just like he'd locked her out of his life.

Julia jumped up from her chair. "I've got to get out of here. It's this house, Mrs. Strong. It's been this house all along." Julia ran out of the kitchen, her heels clattering down the hallway.

The front door slammed shut and a few moments later a car started and drove away.

After washing and drying Julia's tea cup and returning it to the cupboard, Mrs. Strong crossed the kitchen to open the door to the pantry. Jack's still body was slumped in front of the shelves, blood from a chest wound stained his grey sweatshirt and pooled on the floor. Mrs. Strong retrieved the folded newspaper beside his body and then picked up the phone to dial 911.

"Yes," she told the dispatcher, "I have an emergency to report. I just saw my next-door neighbor drive away from her house in great distress. When I came over to see if anything was wrong, I found her husband in the kitchen pantry. I—I think he's dead." Mrs. Strong paused for effect. "The address is 122 Fairhaven Lane. You may already know it. It's the Warren house."

When she finished the call, Mrs. Strong sat down to wait for the police. She pulled out a photograph from the pocket of her dress and placed it on the kitchen table in front of her:

two small smiling children sat in front of their father on a redwood deck

Mrs. Strong looked toward the doorway through which Julia had fled and then turned back to the picture. "I hope they believe her, Leo," she said softly. "I really hope they do. I had to help her along, of course, but she can blame it on the house. And maybe if the police believe her, they'll realize that you didn't kill your family, either. Like she said, it's this house. It's always been this house."

Meredith Davies Hadaway

HERE AFTER

My neighbor died three months ago
but her grown children cannot bring themselves
to sell the house. Instead they've rigged the place

with timers. At five o'clock the living room
lights up for cocktails. At six the kitchen's
brightness signals the beginning of the evening

meal. By ten the bedroom window glows
in case one wants to read in bed.
And so the house—its cupboards packed

with earthly goods, the car still in the drive—lives on
as timers orbit notch by notch around their dials.
One night a shape behind the shade

pulsed and flickered and stopped me
cold until I recognized the random rhythm
of the evening news. Later

I watched a large, gray cat leap once
and disappear behind foundation plantings.
How nice, I thought, the house

has taken in a stray—though I worry now:
is the cat finding food? Is the house watching
too much television? This week's snowstorm has kept me

home for three straight days. I pace from room
to room while the river rises, and drifts
climb the walls. The house next door, gone white,

goes on turning on and off. No one in, no one
out. No footprints. Just a wisp of smoke hanging
over the chimney like breath in the cold.

Meredith Davies Hadaway

AS IF HAPPINESS WERE SKY

Jessica Barksdale

"We all have needs," Diane tells her husband over breakfast, as if the conversation from last night were ongoing. "People want things."

Diane watches Jim eat his scrambled eggs. One by one, she picks up her toast crumbs with a wet fingertip.

"People want too much." He folds his newspaper and looks up at her over his reading glasses. He waits, takes off his glasses, clicks them closed. "Money, power, love, happiness. A way to make the past disappear. A way to be forgiven."

"Who wouldn't want that?" She licks an index finger.

"Enough is enough, don't you think?"

"But we never have enough," she says.

"What about food, water, shelter?" he says. "What could you possibly want?"

"People still want even if they have."

"You want something you don't even know the name of," he says. "You think like someone being served cake who wants something sweeter."

"Well, you think like an asshole."

Diane pushes back the barstool and stands up, walks to the recycling bin, tosses in his newspaper. He's right, as usual. She talks out of privilege because she can and because they've had this fight for thirty years. She knows he will forgive her. "Look, I'm sorry. You're right. But my having cake doesn't mean I shouldn't want something else. This has been proven before."

He shakes his head, puts down his fork. If he weren't on a barstool, he'd recline. If he smoked a pipe, he'd take in a big draw, exhaling in smoke rings. If he drank in the mornings, he'd shoot back a large snort of Glenfiddich. "I don't want to move."

"I know what I want. I know what I can have."

"I don't want to move."

She sighs, rinses the sink, orange juice and eggshell swirling the stainless steel sink. All her life, she's lived in the Bay Area, every day one long journey from traffic jam to traffic jam. The only good news is that online teaching, keeping her at home a couple of days a week instead spending of four days on campus. What she dreams of now is retirement and a large flat lot where their dog Lulu can run within the confines of a good fence. A lot of yard and sun and no one next door.

"I like this house," he says. "I like our life here. Our children live close. Eventually, at least one of them is going to have kids. There's room for visitors. Your mom is here. Where are we going to go that will be easy for any of them to get to us? Anyway, you picked out this house in the first place."

She nods.

"I need to keep working."

"You need to keep working to live here."

He nods.

She's about to tell him something dark, a sentence lodged in her chest, something like, "I'm going to go, with or without you." But she doesn't because she's unsure if she means it. Or unsure if once she means it, she will know what to do about it.

Jessica Barksdale

"I've got to go to work," he says, handing her his plate. "We can talk more about this—"

"Until it doesn't happen."

He shrugs, walks around the counter, kisses her on the temple. "Or until it does. For now, please just buy a damn couch or something."

Later, she's in her home office, looking out onto cypress, oak, and maple trees, the world gone autumn, light greens, oranges, reds, big magenta berries on the strawberry tree. Lulu likes to eat them, and though the berries aren't poisonous, they make her a gaseous olfactory terror. Yesterday, Diane climbed up into the tree and shook it hard and then collected all the berries she could, big gloppy blobs, soft as tiny, overripe papayas. Somehow, though, the tree keeps giving and Lulu keeps eating, enough so that Diane sometimes locks her behind the baby gates in the kitchen.

But now—furry, white, slightly panting—Lulu is asleep at her feet, and Diane opens her browser and heads to her favorites: *Real Estate Sonoma, Real Estate Mendocino, Real Estate Charlotte, Real Estate Charleston, Real Estate Paris*. Actually, the favorites go on, but she's mostly narrowed her search, focusing on doable local areas and dream locales based on beloved vacations. In half of her imaginings, Jim is with her, living happy in Sonoma on a half-acre, working on his computer in a back room while she and Lulu frolic in the large yard. In the other half, she and Lulu have driven by car across the country to Diane's new home on a shaded Charleston street. At night, she makes shrimp dishes and drinks white wine, first alone, but then with her friendly neighbors and new colleagues at the local college that hired her despite her age. She's bought a giant king-sized bed and lets Lulu sleep right next to her, something Jim forbids. Sometimes, Diane goes for days without talking to anyone, padding around on the smooth hardwood floors, drinking dark coffee from new mugs, and watching all the period-piece dramas that Jim sighs at. She eats nonfat yogurt for dinner and ham sandwiches whenever she feels like it. She wears her gym clothes a lot and forgets to polish her toenails.

Now, though, she clicks on *Real Estate Sonoma.*

And, of course, she finds the one. There it is, big and yellow and wrap-around porched. Four bedrooms, three bathrooms. A chef's kitchen sleek with granite counters and an island and stainless steel appliances. A guest house for her mother and their children. A yard for the tomatoes she can't grow in Oakland with all the fog and wind. Conveniently located near the town square, close to restaurants and shops and the highway, the one she can travel on should she need to zip back to the Bay Area fast. And flat, for the walker she will need one day. So there are three porch steps. But in the back? A flat way into the house, a place she can rest in. A place she can die in, too.

Only 1.95 million dollars for this perfection.

Diane picks up her cell phone. Under her feet, Lulu stretches. Both of them are ready for a drive.

Isn't it just divine?" Casey, the local agent, says as she opens the large wooden front door, weathered and worn, even though the house was built in 2008. Diane doesn't ask, but she assumes it was made from wine casks or barn doors or sailing boat hulls, the lumber reclaimed, reused, refabbed. "And so close to the square."

Diane turns to look back at Lulu, who is tied to the porch rail by her leash and sits next to a full bowl of water. Lulu wags her tail and waits. When Diane doesn't move toward her, she slumps to the smooth, porch, painted burgundy, the same color as the trim.

"I'll be back," Diane tells Lulu, but the dog closes her eyes, Diane clearly dead to her until they get back into the car.

Diane turns back toward the house and walks through the door onto an acre of gleaming hardwood. The windows almost crackle, bright like the diamonds they must have cost, the painted white crown molding and chair rails and wainscoting is almost too bright to look at.

"Built in 2008, it was based on the original home on site. Thirty-three hundred square feet plus the guest house. A total writer's retreat." The agent, Casey, clacks through the living room down the shining floor. Diane follows behind, holding her breath as she takes in the carefully staged furnishings, the deep, plush fabrics, the heavy, crafted furniture, the shine of bowl and spoon and lamp. She stops, makes and turn, and then exhales and takes in a shuddering breath.

"The kitchen," Casey calls out. "Totally up-to-date. All top-of-the-line appliances. Some I'm sure you won't know what to do with. Two! Two, count them, warming drawers! Two full sized ovens. A wine cellar, a wine refrigerator, a wine rack. Two full-sized sinks. Two disposals. A full-sized fridge and freezer. A chef's delight!"

Diane glides into the kitchen, slipping lightly across the sleek granite floors. Her palms graze every surface. Outside each window, a shock of green, sprays of white, yellow, orange, red, the winds calm, the sky blue.

Casey pulls her onward, through the large bedrooms with their cushy carpet, into the bathrooms as big as Diane's home office, past common areas with bookshelves and nooks and window seats. In the backyard, just there under the redwood tree, the guest cottage, a warm yellow light beckoning from the large front window. For a second, Diane holds her arms out as she glances upward, eyes closed. The air smells like summer hills and pine needles. On her skin, the sun is warm, the air light. Under her feet, the lawn is even better than the million dollar carpet in the bedrooms.

"Can you imagine the garden you could have right there?" Casey says.

Yes, Diane thinks. She can.

Jessica Barksdale

Later in a café on the square, a wood and glass and organic place full of sunshine on the corner of First and West Napa, Diane does math, never her strength. Lulu is under the table, at Diane's feet, gnawing on a carrot dental treat that occupies her for exactly twenty-four minutes. Diane sighs, knowing she needs to work fast. In college, she was able to fulfill graduation requirements by taking Math for Liberal Arts Students, a class crafted of consumer math with a smattering of Algebra, a language she never learned to speak. Her teacher called her English Major, though in reality, he said "Engrish Maja." He looked to her for explanations and translations, and cried out in dismay when the class laughed at his pronunciation of "Penus butta."

He gave her a C, a credit, a pass, when she deserved a D and another semester (at least) of stabbing at the calculator.

Here she is again, but unlike in class, she's not trying to figure out which jar of peanut butter is cheaper, but how to afford an almost two-million dollar house.

"Here you go," the cute server says, setting down Diane's cappuccino and bran muffin. His head is shaved as is his face, his shirt white, sleeves rolled, apron black and folded in an origami-like way around his waist. This town is filled with cafes and restaurants with young attractive people serving older people and tourists. All around her are cheesemongers and trinket stores and ice cream parlors. Galleries and designer boutiques. T-shirts flap from open storefront windows. Disneyland but with wine.

"Thanks." She sips her coffee, tries to imagine what twenty percent of 1.95 million is. Four hundred thousand? She thinks it's four hundred thousand, unable to believe the decimal point could be so inconsistent. Four hundred thousand dollars she has, but then what was the mortgage on 1.55 million? Seven thousand a month? She tries to calculate some more, but she's unclear about current interest rates not to mention the different kinds of mortgages. Further, does she multiply or divide? With the money her father left her when he died eight years ago, she could put down twenty percent or even more and pay the mortgage for a couple years. Three, maybe. Because of an identity theft nightmare five years ago, Jim's and her finances have been cleverly cleft in twain—no paper or digital trail that leads back to Jim's paycheck or credit cards or tax information—and an inheritance goes with the inheritor. The problem would be getting a loan and then trying to stay married once Jim finds out what she'd been up to with the money he assumes will be part of their retirement.

She turns off the calculator and calls her friend Bettina, a high-profile Oakland Hills real estate agent, who has rebounded from the 2008 economy debacle and sold ten houses this year all over asking with multiple offers. She drives a black Jaguar and lives in a house with a moat.

"You're insane," Bettina says after Diane is done explaining. "What the hell are you doing?"

Lulu licks Diane's left foot and then goes back to her carrot chew.

"I'm not sure."

"Then for god's sake get back into your car and come home." Diane hears the suck of Bettina's cigarette inhale. "Get the hell out of that wine infested hell-hole."

"I can't do anything. It's not like I can write up an offer," Diane says. "I don't even know what interest rates are."

"Does Jim know you're even looking at houses?"

"No. He doesn't want a second home. You know that."

"Are you sure it's a second home?" Bettina asks.

Diane wishes she had her own cigarette, a habit she gave up the same semester she took math, the semester she got pregnant with Rob.

"What the hell is the sale price again?"

Diane tells her.

"Jesus," Bettina says.

"I know."

There's a pause, another suck, a long throaty exhale. "Where the hell are you exactly?"

By the time the house closes, Diane has constructed a solid lie platform. Suddenly, she's taken over two classes on campus, strangely spaced apart. An 8 a.m. and 7 p.m., Tuesday and Thursday. That gives her almost 15 hours to be absent. Somehow, also, she's convinced Jim that campus rules have changed about dogs.

"New social views. Service dogs are in. For the blind. The mentally ill," she says.

"You don't need a service dog," he says, an unspoken—she thinks—yet in the air.

"Maybe I do."

He's silent, holding his whiskey glass with thumb and forefinger.

Diane presses on. "So basically, I'll keep Lulu in her crate when I'm in class. Then we'll do walkies around the campus."

Jim looks at her, his gaze level, unblinking. "You've been trying to get off campus for years. You reach that balance, and there you are again. Remember how it was when the kids were little?"

"Look, it was an emergency. My colleague. Well, she, well, she kind of lost it. I'm doing the chair a favor."

Jim nods. "How long?"

"Till the end of the semester. Hopefully she'll be better by spring."

Jim looks at her, sips his drink.

At first, she uses the long stretch of day to meet Bettina at her office and sign forms. Then there are road trips in the black Jaguar up to Sonoma for inspections, which are followed by rounds of negotiations, the price dropping once, and then again when the roof problem literally came to light. When all was settled and done, Diane buys the house for 1.55 million, with the owners—a couple who own a local winery—covering the closing costs, an amount that pays for another year of mortgage payments.

"I don't feel good about this. And I still say you're crazy," Bettina said on the way down from their last visit to the house together. "Don't even invite me up for cocktails until this is over or you're divorced. I can't be responsible for what I say. You know I like Jim. I'll tell him what a loon he's married."

But then, that first day, her new key in her hand, Diane walked into the empty, unfurnished house, and understood that Jim had been right all along. People want too much.

She knew she was right, too. People have needs. And she needs this house.

Now Diane sits on one of the two chairs she brought into the house, cast-offs she'd tucked into the basement of the Oakland house years ago. She's hooked up the electricity, gas, and water. The garbage is picked up on Wednesdays, three different colored barrels dropped off the day before. She's gone to the local store and purchased whole bean coffee to go along with the coffee grinder and machine she bought at Macy's on the way up. On the roof, men crawl around, patching the hole where the rain seeped in and caused rot and cutting another where she wants a skylight, the attic room crying for more light. Next week, men are coming to replace some bad plumbing and fix the electrical outlets in all the bedrooms. In the backyard, Lulu sleeps in the shade of a persimmon tree, the leaves turning orange, almost red. Overhead, the sky is a light tight blue.

Diane has connected the Internet, so she sits on one of the chairs and uses the kitchen counter as a desk. She's shopping for a bed, not that she can ever sleep here. In her Crate and Barrel shopping basket is a bed frame named *Caroline* and all the accessories Diane needs to go along with it: sheets, pillows, comforter, shams, duvet cover. She's moved onto dining room tables, and she knows that she will need chairs as well. At least for the imaginary parties she will have with the people she can't invite. But the online catalogue presents scene after scene of staged whimsy, and she adds a couple of lamps, a coffee table, kitchen towels, dinner plates, a reading chair to her shopping cart.

"Ma'am," one of the workers calls from the open front door.

Diane looks up and sees him in the doorway. She pushes away from the counter and walks to him, her steps echoing in the empty house.

"All done," he says as she nears him.

Diane looks over the invoice, writes the company a check, and walks out to the front yard as the man and the other workers pack up their tools and then drive away. She can't spot the patched hole—a good thing—but she can see the new skylight, a white square eye hanging on the roof. Lulu comes patting around from the back and sits at her feet, her back against Diane's shin. Her dog is warm, the air, too. The sun is a perfect round orb, the shrubs shiny and emerald, the grass in the meadow across the street long and lime green. The house is the most perfect color of yellow, warm and filled with white. It glows like an afternoon-ripened lemon hanging on a tree. The sycamore tree sways, once leaf, two, falling, cupped palms holding air.

How are the new classes going?" Jim asks at dinner. When she looks up from her plate, Diane sees that he's staring at her hands, her fingernails rimmed with Citrus Cream, the color she's been painting one of the upstairs bathrooms. When the morning sun hits the bathroom, Diane feels like she's cocooned inside a lemon meringue pie. But today as she finished up, she forgot to scrub her fingers with the vegetable brush she bought for just this reason.

But she doesn't move her hands, keeping the evidence in plain sight. "Exhausting. I must have been crazy to say yes. But Mary really needed help."

She's invented Mary for her own use. But this doesn't really matter. Jim hasn't gone to a Christmas party or end-of-the year bash for at least a decade. He's unlikely to run into any of her colleagues now that he's so busy at work. A rare strange grocery store, BART, College Avenue surprise interaction is unlikely. But if it happens, Diane could talk about Mary, a new part-time teacher, someone her full-time colleagues would accept not knowing.

Jim's still looking at her hands. Diane glances down, too, noticing not only the paint but the calluses and reddened skin from working in the garden, stripping wallpaper from the powder room, and putting up shelves in the potting shed. She picks up her fork, spears a small marinated beet, one that she bought in downtown Sonoma on her way home, the take away box smashed flat and hidden in the recycling bin.

Diane's created a checklist of lies, obfuscations, and cover-ups in her mind, a litany she goes over every day she drives home from the house:

Throw away receipts and store bags on car floor.
Get gas in Oakland.
Brush Lulu.
Talk about school/Mary/student essays.
Don't act too happy.
Make sure to have work clothes on. Carry briefcase, papers, books.
Complain about everything.

There's nothing she can do about the odometer, but Jim rarely drives her Volvo. If he does notice the additional miles per week, she'll say she sometimes comes home from school on those long days. Or goes shopping at the mall. Or has lunch with friends in Berkeley. At night, she thinks about all the ways she can be caught. A customer service call about her loan or one of the deliveries at the Sonoma house. A report about a fire late at night in the guest house. What if one wet day, she skids to her death on Highway

121? Jim would be left with a house he didn't even know existed. One night, she sneaks out of bed and types up a letter, telling him how to access the loan, the utility bulls, the insurance online. She organizes an envelope with the deed and the letter apologizing for her insanity and puts it at the back of her drawer, hidden under her annuity folder. Eventually, Jim will find out, but she won't have to be alive to witness the aftermath.

But now? She just wants to eat dinner and get him to forget about fingernails.

"These are good, aren't they?" She holds up the beet. "And this sirloin and arugula salad?"

Jim nods, blinks, and goes back to his meal, eating his beets, his lettuce, buttering his sourdough bread.

Diane chews and thinks about the Sonoma house glowing yellow in the streetlight, bats circling around the fir trees in loops, the moon a full wide eye overhead, shining on everything.

At night as she lies awake and after worrying about how not to be discovered, she wonders why she's doing this. Twenty off-and-on years of therapy provide no answers to this lunacy. Can she blame having to share a room with her sister Margaret for twelve long years? But wait. Who didn't share a room back then? Houses weren't like they are now, her childhood home three bedroom, one bath, at least until they added on the master suite, just in time for Diane to head off to college. Margaret was a mean sister, prone to sneak hair pulling and taunts, but no more so than other older sisters. So is it Diane's long marriage to Jim? Did they get married too quickly? Kids too soon? But how could that be an issue now, the boys gone, she and Jim rattling around in it like loose marbles. Perhaps, she thinks, as she turns on her side away from Jim's snores, it's simple and clichéd. Menopause. Lack of hormones cause women to buy million dollar homes. If the cash is available, put it away or else beware Sonoma, Mendocino, Carmel. Menopausal women keep the economy alive. Buying houses, shopping, doing away with diets and eating what they want.

"What?" Jim mumbles.

"What?" she asks, just as she realizes she's been laughing, the sound slight in the room like memory. But just like that, he falls back asleep.

What? she thinks. What does she want?

Lulu stands and then curls again in her bed. The Oakland night grows long and faint, and Diane hides under the covers, waits till day.

Somehow, she's convinced the Composition Committee to drive to Sonoma for a day-long retreat. She told them the house is a friend's second home, and for the very first time in ages, she's told Jim the truth about where she is going.

"We need to hash out this stuff before the semester ends," she says as she packs up her and Lulu's bags. "We need a whole day."

"Pretty fancy for a work meeting," Jim says. "Too bad the weather isn't great for the drive."

Diane nods. Fall is rounding into winter, the rainy season started. Highway 121 is dangerous and slick at times, and Diane has found herself staying home on days she might have driven up to the house. The good news is that all the repair work has been done. The bedrooms are furnished with beds and dressers and colored quilts and duvet covers. Fluffy towels hang in the bathrooms, soft bath mats underfoot. The fridge is filled with what Diane needs during her visits, and today as she waits for her colleagues, she pulls out butter and jam and the fresh pastries and bread she's bought at the bakery in the square.

"My God," her longtime colleague Gail says as she wipes her feet on the front mat and stares into the house. "What a house! I can't believe they don't live here fulltime. And that they don't have to rent it out 30 days a month just to break even."

"He's in technology. Silicon Valley somewhere." Diane takes Gail's coat, hangs it on the new coat rack, plucking a sycamore leaf off her lapel. "And she's in corporate law."

"Enough said," Gail says. "Clearly, they aren't teachers."

The comments are the same when the others arrive, Diane taking them all on a tour of lies, explaining her friends' amazing lives and careers, their trips to Africa and China and Bhutan, their two kids—one Yale, one Wesleyan—their grandchild on the way. This house, she tells them, is nothing to their place in Palo Alto. And their Tahoe cabin, right on the water? Don't even ask about it.

But then they all sit down at the large brand-new cherry table, eat muffins and bread and croissants and plan out the composition courses for the next two semesters and the faculty retreat where they will revise writing standards. Then over an arugula salad and chilled grilled tuna, they gossip about colleagues not present, bitch about the union and the college president, and share family updates. Finally, Diane's alone in the house, the sleek silver dishwasher whispering, the table and counter cleared and cleaned, Lulu asleep in her bed in the corner of the kitchen. In just fifteen minutes, Diane will have to leave, too. But all she wants to do is sit at the island, stare out into the backyard. All she wants to do is stay, a longing in her chest that can't be about the house. The rip of sadness yanks at her, and she sits down on one of the chairs she ordered from Crate and Barrel—Rachelle—and cries.

At first, her tears are more like sniffles, but then she's crying as she does sometimes when she dreams about her father. In her reoccurring dream, Diane is always her childhood self—ten or eleven—her age when he first got sick. There he is, standing in front of her, still strong, still whole, the man whose laugh was so loud, it filled the house from kitchen to bedroom hallway. He's always laughing in the dream, at least at first. But then, he stops, his body slumps, folds into a small humped letter C. As she watches him shuffle away from her, the dream Diane breathes in the smells of the rest of her childhood, the tang of alcohol and PineSol covering up his foul odors, the tang covering up the messes he would make of himself and anywhere he sat. In her dream and probably in real life, she runs from the smells, from him, holding her face and crying as she does, sobbing until she wakes up and pulls out of the past, even though she knows that time is stuck inside her like a terrible arrow.

Diane stops crying when Lulu leans up against her legs, her dog body warm and soft. Lulu licks Diane's hand and then slumps down to sleep. Diane wipes her eyes, sits back against the chair seat. Her father lived a long, sick, incapacitated, uncomfortable life. All the while, he'd kept working for his family's business, doing well enough to leave Diane's mother, Diane, and Margaret a small fortune, even though he'd been in an assisted living facility for almost twenty years before he died.

But he'd been big once. Huge. He'd been the most enormous thing in Diane's life, and all she ever wanted to do was live inside his belly laugh. Float as if his happiness were sky.

In the garage back in Oakland, Diane goes through the motions of her checklist, finally deciding not to worry as Jim knows where she's been anyway. Lulu clatters down the steps and rushes into the house through the dog door. From the steps, Diane can hear Jim cooing at her, and the sound yanks at the tears she packed away earlier. He'd made that same sound with their children. As Diane spread flat and delirious on the mattress after being up all night nursing, he'd pick them up and coo into their tiny ears. It was the one sound she could tolerate, knowing that Jim could soothe any baby back to sleep.

Once in the kitchen, Diane puts her bags and briefcase on the counter and starts to say something. But her mouth pulls down at the corners, and she finds herself almost falling onto a barstool. She puts her head in her hands, tries to swallow so she can bear to look up. But she can't.

"Jim," she says from the cave of her hands. "I have to tell you something."

There's a pause. Lulu's doggie tags stop tinkling. Diane hears Jim stand, move toward her.

"You know," he says, hands on her shoulders, pressing. "I know."

Sandra Sidman Larson

CROSSROADS NEAR LAKE AND DREW

Minneapolis, Minnesota

Homeless men walk the tracks behind my house,
occasionally shouting to each other, or to no one.
I walk here too; toss up words like birds into taut air.

At the edge of my eye I see him standing by
the silver ribbons—a red fox—pointed ears,
black eyes, fur of train-track. color. He stares
at me. I stare at him, accept his dare.

He turns, saunters off into the late
summer grasses. The sumac flashing
its fingers, and I follow its flare,
turning under a bridge that spans the tracks

and come upon abandoned, faded fires
of exhausted men. Only a warbler still lingers,
sits on a weed pod, picking at his breast.
My footsteps in the gravel startle him.

From under the bridge's blackened arches
a choir of pigeons take flight. The fox is gone,
has left me with miles either of us could go
from here. I think about men, living outside,

like the fox, people long ago walking with deerskin
footsteps, and I know it would take
a certain strength, some fire,
to walk through a world without rooms.

Sandra Sidman Larson

COVENANTS

Tom Miller Juvik

Here in the soiled heart of Harbor Heights, there is no more Sharon-and-Jimmer. The two-story home I once shared with my wife and two children perches on a rise, the center house among five that circumscribe the cul-de-sac. I command the high ground. From the window of my study, I look down into the living rooms of four homes and the front porches of eight others down the street. Beyond that, hundreds of acres of designer homes, all carefully crafted and maintained according to the covenants that dictate the terms of our personal surrender to the community in which we reside.

In the distance, Mt. Rainier presides over the churning waters of Puget Sound, but I hardly give it a glance as Gordon Spillinger's chocolate Lab snuffles his way through the yellow, ankle-high grass that surrounds my front walk. He follows his nose, eventually squatting near the overturned birdbath. The window of my den is open, and it is a simple matter to lift the pellet gun from my desk and draw a bead. A couple of quick pops send the animal scampering between houses.

I cannot help but laugh. In simpler times, Gordon and Peggy Spillinger were at the top of my shit list because they allowed their dog Rudy to run rampant, pissing and crapping all over my carefully groomed lawn. Now that nothing about my life is carefully groomed, dunderheads like the Spillingers are the least of my concerns. I merely drill the simple-minded beast for drill. If I had been serious about nailing Rudy, I would have drawn my holstered .45 or grabbed one of the two semi-automatics lined up along the wall in front of the window—the BAR or the Ruger .44 carbine.

For now, the bolt-action Winchester is out of the question; I have her broken down for cleaning. When I was fifteen, she dropped my first elk, a twelve-point buck. I remember standing over the monumental animal, watching life huff from its nostrils sweet and palpable on the chill forest air. When I was done heaving all over the huckleberry bushes, the buck was still trying to thrash its way up from dark, frozen earth, eyes rolling with a high octane mixture of pain and adrenaline.

The old man grasped the barrel of my Winchester and swung it toward the buck's forehead. "Finish him."

I looked away.

"You bring a rifle to the party, it's on you to close the deal."

I pumped a mercy bullet into the animal's skull, and the forest went quiet, the sound of the shot echoing far into the hills for so long, I did not think it would ever stop.

"After the first death, there is no other," Dylan Thomas wrote. Although I never completed my degree in literature, I know enough to understand he was not addressing the prospect of pulling the trigger. Still, in the context of my personal experience, the line applies. I am a man who has gone on many hunts since murdering that buck in the emerald green forests of the Olympics, and I took the lessons I learned with me into the initial hot, sandblasted surge of Desert Storm. During that first kill, my old man helped me understand the moral necessity of finality, and in its presence, I have not felt the slightest hitch in my stomach since that day.

The Spillingers and their crap-happy dog have nothing to fear from me; they are not worth the gunpowder. Even when I disliked them most, I pitied them; they have always seemed like outsiders in Harbor Heights, our gated community on the hillside overlooking the shores of Port Defiance. During those innocent years before I knew what hate really was, the ritual of tending our yards while the kids roller-skated in the cul-de-sac served as a prelude to barbecue parties that rollicked the summer nights or progressive dinners that often added too many spirits to the holiday season. Including the Spillingers on the guest list was an obligation no one relished.

Sharon and I were their opposites, standing near the center of this social swirl. People called me Jimmer, then. Sharon and Jimmer Grassi. Just as I am bronze-skinned, dark-haired, full-blooded Italian, Sharon is pure Norwegian with hair so blonde, it seems diaphanous when the sunlight hits it just right. Everyone loved her in those days, some more than others, and that is what killed our daughter Amy.

According to the protective covenants governing our community, residents must keep their yards neatly groomed. Garbage cans may not be visible from the street except on pick-up days. Cars and boats must be garaged, never parked in the driveway or street overnight. Landscaping changes and home remodels, including paint colors, must be submitted to the almighty Homeowners Association for approval. These and countless other b.s. rules help maintain the b.s. façade of this staid, upstanding, upscale b.s. community. Not exactly the wide-open West that once summoned pioneers.

But spring is in the air, and my unkempt lawn is riddled with bright yellow dandelions that shout dissension. My dirt-caked Lexus has been dripping oil by the curb for a week, and the half-finished paintjob on the front side of the house is this gawd-awful pink especially selected to provoke the powers-that-be. After numerous warnings, members of the Homeowners Association have taken the bait, announcing by certified mail that they will be dropping by at 3:00 this afternoon to inspect the premises. If I am still not in compliance (and there really is no "if" about it), they will begin legal proceedings that will result in stiff penalties beyond the unpaid fines already assessed against me. In the interest of efficiency, I have also scheduled this time for Sharon and her pompous-ass attorney to conduct the walk-through they have been demanding. The attorney's letterhead missive states they are hopeful this will result in an accurate inventory of our belongings and a quick, amicable division of property. Yeah, right.

During the month since my career as advertising director at Barley and Gordon tanked, I have had ample opportunity to ponder the hypocrisy that directs the affairs of Harbor Heights; plenty of time to mull over how I lost my wife Sharon and wonder why my 16-year-old daughter Amy had to die in a car wreck.

Someone moves across the Tingstads' living room, and I grab my binoculars. "Is that you, Jared, you sick little piece of shit?"

I study the faces of family members and two visitors through the silk curtains three houses down from ours. No sign of Jared, but that does not mean he is not roaming some other room in the blue split-level. "The Murderer." That's what Sharon and I used to call him before I learned that she was the catalyst for our daughter's demise, more worthy of blame than the sad-ass punk behind the wheel of a VW Jetta with bald tires.

Although Jared Tingstad is 24 years old, he still lives with his parents while he floats continually between jobs and joblessness. His bedroom is on the side of the house closest to ours, and when my kids were little, we used to share a laugh whenever we spotted him sneaking out the window at night. His parents are alcoholics who have always allowed him to run wild. More than once, they have lied to protect him from arrest or prosecution, the reason why I do not consider them innocent in the matter of Amy's death.

Jared suffered a broken clavicle and a variety of contusions in the car wreck that took my daughter's life, but "suffered" hardly seems the right word. The law has yet to punish him for reckless driving or charge him with statutory rape for having intercourse with a minor. After my afternoon visitors have arrived and departed in a way far more permanent than they anticipate, I intend to complete the job the courts have left unfinished.

Across the street from the Tingstads, Marlene Robertson steps out of the house to tend the plant boxes framing her front porch. She is a silver-haired woman whose childish, cutie-pie face seems incompatible with her overwhelming breasts and inviting hips. Her husband Jack serves as president of The Homeowners Association, which consists of four elected community members and a representative from Harbor Heights Development Corporation. In their spare time, they settle disputes and enforce the covenants that govern the 400 acres that comprise our community. These cutthroat pirates compensate themselves with a handsome honorarium from the mandatory membership dues we pay for the privilege of living in what the real estate brochure describes as "...a master-planned haven far from the hectic realities of the outside world." Just enough money remains to operate a small office at the clubhouse and cover the salaries of a property manager who presides over a secretary/receptionist, a landscaping crew, and an "inspector" who patrols our streets in a golf cart, on alert for any untrimmed hedge that might signal potential anarchy.

The sovereignty of the Homeowners Association extends to a paved jogging trail that snakes through the development and several common areas, including a park complete with playground, picnic area, tennis courts, swimming pool, and softball diamond. A gym and nine-hole golf course are in the works if the Association can purchase a few more family farms. Membership will be compulsory for all residents. Jack Robertson and I used to be teammates on the slo-pitch team his real estate company sponsors. Then, last spring, he informed me the team had a new first baseman—a bigger, younger man named Hal who recently moved into the new subdivision to the north. I used to think the recreation league was about having fun, bringing neighbors closer together. A misconception on my part.

Needless to say, Jack was moving rapidly up my shit list even before I discovered he was having an affair with Sharon. But my wife's infidelity and the knowledge that it precipitated my daughter's death became the real game-changer, the fundamental betrayal that rendered all vows, covenants, and principles of civilized behavior null and void. Goodbye Social Contract; hello, State of Nature.

Jack's wife Marlene appointed herself the bearer of this particular bad tiding a respectable three weeks after Amy's funeral, appearing on my doorstep one night when Sharon claimed to be playing Bunco with some of the gals she works with at the county courthouse. Marlene was wearing a long, silver fox fur coat, her eyes glistening with a mixture of tears and Tanqueray as she rushed past me into the house. There, in front of the blue flames of our gas fireplace, she tossed aside the coat to reveal a red teddy and fishnet stockings.

"Hold me, Jimmer." She wrapped her arms around my neck, grinding her pelvis against mine. "Take me anyway you want me."

I grasped her elbows and settled her onto the couch, where she turned sloppy. That was when she told me that Jack and Sharon had been carrying on ever since my son Davie headed back to college after spring break.

"They are together as we speak," she claimed in a stolid way that I could not disbelieve.

I poured each of us a scotch and settled into the recliner across from her. A sort of numbness had settled over me after losing my little girl on a wet road a month earlier. Now, the news that my wife had betrayed me cut through this thick insulation and burned against my ribs. I asked Marlene to start her story from the beginning, wondering if there would come a point where I would take her by the hand and lead her into the bedroom to try and heal old wounds by opening new ones.

After a time, she drained her glass and scooted up on the couch, taking too long to run her tongue along her lips, as though relishing the taste of her own words. "He was here, in your bed with your wife the night Amy died."

I found myself on my feet, fists doubled, shoulders swelling till they ached.

"Pour me another drink, would you, Jimmer." Her lips budded into something resembling a kiss.

I handed her the bottle, then settled back into my chair, hands forming a tense steeple beneath my nose.

"Jack told me everything—how you were at a convention in Chicago and Amy was at a sleepover with friends. And I…well, this was one of those nights when I tried to drink myself to sleep."

"The short version, please."

She nodded, as though understanding that there would be nothing between the two of us except this. "Amy's sleepover turned out to be a lie. She was out with Jared Tingstad. But something must have happened between them because they cut the evening short. That's when she returned home to find her mother in bed with Jack. Before Sharon could even think to cover herself with a sheet, Amy was out the door and on her way to Jared's house."

Marlene took a long sip, waiting to hear what I would say, watching me in anticipation of what I might do. Something in her eyes told me that when her husband crawled back into bed tonight smelling of my wife, she would tell him everything that happened here. Somehow, in their own sick way, this would serve as intimacy.

"I stepped outside in time to see Jared's car fishtailing down the street," she said at last. "Sharon stood at the front door, still pulling on her robe as my husband tried to blend in with the shadows in a sad attempt to slink home undetected."

"You can leave now."

"There's more, Jimmer, so much more that has gone on between them since that night."

"You told me everything I need to know."

She rose from the couch and pulled on her coat. "What will you do?"

"Whatever's necessary."

And that is why I wait at the window, cleaning the rifle that took down my first elk, preparing for guests to cross the threshold of my home. I do not know who will be the first to arrive, but I do know this much: it will begin with them and, somewhere down the road that leads out of this cul-de-sac, it will end with me.

Tom Miller Juvik

APARTMENT 135

Alisa A. Gaston-Linn

My mother does not tell us. We don't know what a divorce is and that she has finally tolerated enough of our father—wetting the bed because he's too drunk to feel his own bladder, lying about the jobs and the money. When she leaves him, she is in her late twenties and we, her daughters, are nine, seven, and two. She files bankruptcy, another term we do not know. She has a high school education and knows shorthand.

Our house, the one with our father in Lakewood Colorado, has three levels, including a balcony that my older sister and her friends jump off of when my mother is out, landing on a black vinyl beanbag on the family room carpet. I had the chickenpox once and spent days on the couch in that family room, staring admiringly at the massive stone wall that reached up from the fireplace to the ceiling, each stone decorated with patches of cornflake shaped, green moss that had begun its life where the stones first originated.

We move from that lovely home with lush grass on the lawns, pleasantly situated in the middle of a cul-de-sac, open and perfect for all of us neighborhood kids to play kick-the-can and hide-and-seek on summer nights giftedly lit with silver stars and complete with crickets chirping. We move into the shitty apartment complex.

They are rectangular buildings painted a lackluster brown, with piss yellow trim. Piss yellow security doors. Flat roofs, as though incomplete, another project taking precedence over the structures that house the unfortunate. But I do not know, yet, that I am that.

I carry boxes from our Pinto station wagon, the car my grandparents bought for my mother, to the second floor into apartment 135. I walk into a tiny front room that will now be our family room. It takes me eight steps to go from the front room to our kitchen that is boxed into a corner, cut off from the rest of the place. A sliding glass door opens to a balcony about seven feet by five feet—it will be the future place of my mother's hanging chair made of rattan, designed like a round bird cage missing a side. I do not know as I stand on the empty balcony that I will swing in that chair often, using my feet to push off the side of the building, and eventually cause the chair to fall to the "floor" of the balcony with me in it.

I see the one bathroom with a regular door on one side, and a sliding door leading to the "master" bedroom. My mother's king sized bed takes up the entire bedroom, her heavy, wooden dresser with two mirrors is shoved up against one wall and her antique princess phone sits on one end, the phone that I pretend with, the phone that allows me to remove myself from this situation and launch my childhood into a different place, a pretend place with massive stone houses in another country that is drenched in rain and has horses on the lawn. Or back to my previous childhood with bridge parties, homemade Christmas decorations, and sparkly dresses for my mother on Saturday nights while we wait with the sitter. On the other end of her dresser is a round, plastic platter with perfume bottles. Next to it sits her glass jewelry box that I sneak into sometimes to ornament my neck and ears.

My mother shows me our room. It holds two twin-sized beds and one dresser for my sisters and me. I end up sharing one of those twin-sized beds with my little sister for seven years. It is from that which I believe comes my inability to cuddle with my future husband in our queen-sized bed as we sleep. "I need room," I tell him. "I can't sleep if I feel crowded." This hurts him, he does not understand. He cannot comprehend how I spent most of my nights fearful of falling off the edge of the bed, and using my legs and feet to push my sleeping baby sister up against the wall because I was so irritated that I had no room and she slept practically on top of me, her smelly "blankie" wrapping her tiny body, her open mouth breathing little toddler breath in my face. If my husband has his arms wrapped around me while I try to fall asleep, it is like an iron maiden and I feel trapped. I don't tell him this because I am afraid he will leave if he knows the depth of my internal chaos.

An insurance brokerage hires my mother as their secretary so she is gone all day and can only afford daycare for my younger sister. In the afternoons, I walk home from school, use my key to let myself in, grab a Hostess Ding Dong and watch The Brady Brunch on television. At four, I walk to the daycare center and pick up my little sister, and I always take a large spoon of peanut butter. Even though she is only two, I don't hold her hand as we're forced to walk in the middle of the road without a sidewalk on this stretch that reaches from our apartment building to the center. Not because I don't love her, not because of the bed, but because I do not know yet that I am her keeper. It does not calculate in my underdeveloped brain.

Later, much later, when we are older, she tells me that she always watched me eat that peanut butter off the spoon and wanted some "so badly." We also reflect on the dead cat we saw one afternoon while walking back from the daycare center. Stiff and decaying, its position was that of elimination. The cat did not move out of the road simply because it was doing a most natural thing. It still had feces attached.

My little sister goes off to play, and I pull up a chair to the stove because I cannot reach the burners without the chair. I place the large, aluminum frying pan on the burner, take the hamburger out of the fridge, and begin to brown it. Sometimes my older sister starts dinner, but many times she is out with friends from the apartment complex. As I stand on the chair and brown the meat, my mother calls me. I stretch the phone cord so that I can continue to stand on the chair. She tells me she will be home soon and to take out the pasta and boil the water.

The security door to our building remains propped open by a large rock. No one removes it or questions our safety. On the bottom floor, cattycorner to us, lives Sandy. She is another single woman with a deaf daughter, Cathy, my age, and another daughter, Stephanie, my little sister's age. Stephanie has an endless amount of green snot in her nose and even at the age of seven, I remain completely perplexed as to why no one ever wipes that little girl's nose. I cannot look at her for fear that I will vomit.

Cathy and I hang out a lot, but I do not like to be with her. I do not know how to communicate with her and she is always carrying Stephanie and to me, this is a barrier. A crutch, a weight that prohibits Cathy and me to run with the boys because I know I am just as good as those boys. I dump Cathy. But not because we can't run with the boys, because one summer day at the apartment pool, Stephanie is with Sandy on the lounge chairs next to my mother who has red grapes and Pringles potato chips for us to snack on, and I am swimming alone. I look over and Cathy is on the pool steps in the water, sitting next to a little girl who is about three years old. There is a metal railing from the edge of the pool, down the middle of the steps, leading all the way into the water. I see that Cathy and the little girl are playing a game. Cathy goes under water and pretends that she is struggling. The little girl laughs at her each time. Then the little girl goes under the water. I am watching and she is reaching and flailing and trying to find the railing but she cannot find it and she is struggling. Cathy is sitting close to her, laughing. I understand that the little girl is on the verge of drowning so I swim to her. I lift her up and she gasps and coughs and spits water and I place her on the edge and she runs to her mother crying. I look over at Cathy and she looks at me in total confusion. I glare at her. I am angry that she did not understand the girl needed help.

My mother has my older sister and me do the laundry. There are three main doors in each building and the laundry room for us is one door over. On dark winter nights, I carry the laundry basket, and go back and forth on the long sidewalk, walk down the stairs to the basement where the room is, empty clothes into the washer, shove the quarters into the sliding feed, wait to hear the water rush into the barrel, run back to our door, watch the clock, run back to the laundry room, load the wet clothes into the dryer and load more dirty clothes into the washer and run back. For some reason, I do not wear shoes to do this, only socks. Perhaps because I believe that the freezing sidewalk burning my feet will help me run faster. I don't know what is in the dark, but I think there is something evil that will kill a little girl like me. This is why I am angry with my mother for making me do the laundry. This is why I am angry with my mother for making me carry the trash at night from our end of the building to the other end of the building where the dark, sinister dumpster sits with more evil waiting to jump out.

My mother is on a date. We have no babysitter, we understand they do not exist for families who have little money. My sisters and I watch television and at ten-o-clock at night, a man pounds on our door. My older sister tells my younger sister and me to hide. We run to my mother's bedroom and I rummage through her cabinet above the makeshift bathroom in her bedroom, the one that has only a sink and cupboard below, and I find a pair of cuticle scissors. These will be my weapon. I will gouge out his eyes if he breaks into our apartment and tries to kill my sisters and me. I grab my little sister, shove her under my mom's bed, and I fall to my knees on the side of the bed. I lean down, into the carpet. I can smell decades of previous tenants in that brown, shag carpet, no matter how much we have vacuumed, and I hold onto the cuticle scissors tightly as my hands shake. We can hear the man cussing and screaming to open the door as he pounds and pounds. My younger sister cries under the bed. We are all in our cotton pajamas and fuzzy robes like we're waiting for Santa Claus, but this is not jolly Saint Nick at our door. My older sister calls my grandpa who lives fifteen minutes away. He drives over and we hear him talking to the man in the hallway. My grandpa lets himself into our apartment with his key and asks where our mother is. We tell him she's on a date. He shakes his head and tells us that the man was drunk and confused. That he was at the wrong apartment. He asks me what I have in my hands. My shaking hands still hold the tiny, silver scissors and my grandpa smiles at me. I don't know if he's making fun of me or if he's proud of me, but his smile makes all the fear dissolve. He tucks us into bed and waits for my mother to come home.

My grandma comes over every Thursday after school and has my older sister and me help her clean our apartment. She is helping my mother out, and she tells us we need to help her out as well because my mother is working hard. I don't mind doing this; I want to help my mother if it's inside, not outside in the dark. I want her to notice that I am helping. I am your little helper.

Alisa A. Gaston-Linn

For our normal chores my sister and I alternate these two things, 1) vacuuming, and 2) dusting and emptying all trashcans. When my grandma is here, we must clean the bathroom—sink, mirror, toilet, tub—and the kitchen—sink, counters, stove—and we must sweep and mop the bathroom and kitchen floors. Only she will not let us use a mop. She tells us that you cannot clean a floor the right way unless you get on your hands and knees and scrub with a sponge. To this day, I believe she is right, but that does not change the fact that we hated her. Not because she made us clean, but because she was a beast.

My grandma throws away our cherished drawings from school, telling us that they are junk. She tells us that we are ungrateful. She tells us that we are lazy. If this is the beast, my grandpa is the beauty. Every summer, they come to our apartment pool and spend Saturdays with us. While my grandma sits on a chair in the shade, bitching to and about my mother, my grandpa teaches us how to swim. He teaches me how to dive off the side of the pool. Then he teaches me how to dive off the diving board. He teaches me how to do a back dive off the diving board. Finally, he teaches me how to do a back flip off the diving board. He also has us stand on his tan, freckled shoulders, then squats in the water, jumps up, and throws us so we dive far ahead into the pool. This is my beauty.

For my eighth birthday, my mother asks me what I want. She is dating "George" now. His name is Allen, but when we first met him, I asked him what his name was and he told me "George," so it stuck and my sisters and I never call him anything different. I tell my mother I want a tape recorder or a puppy. I had taken a poster out of a kids' magazine and hung it on my wall. Two Silky Terrier puppies in front of a dark red background. I hung the poster on my wall and it held some sort of piece of life that I couldn't seem to reach. A happiness, and simplicity. A piece of life where puppies live with big brown eyes and soft fur and there is no such thing as divorce because the background is rich in color. I know there is no way my mother is going to buy me a puppy but I have nothing to lose.

The day of my birthday, George takes us to Mr. Steak. I order deep fried butterfly shrimp with a large baked potato, butter and sour cream plopped on top, and I dip those shrimp in as much cocktail sauce as I can possibly fit onto the breaded crust. We get home and my mother tells me to sit on the floor for my present. I sit down and wonder why I have to be on the floor to open a box with a tape recorder. I open the box and something tiny jumps out and runs around the apartment so fast I cannot see it. "What is it?" I ask. My mother and George laugh. "It's a puppy!" My mother shrieks. I have so much bliss it is shoving my gut into a bloated mess and I look over at my older sister and she glares at me and I know I will get one of her beatings tonight. But right now, I am watching this itty-bitty Silky Terrier puppy flash through her new home and the smile on my face is real.

While my mother cleans out the fish tank the next day, she asks me what I want to name the puppy. I want her to tell me what she wants it to be but she tells me it is my puppy so it is my choice. I love candy, so I name her Taffy.

Every day after school I take Taffy with me as I wander around the apartment complex. I keep her on a leash sometimes, other times I let her run loose because she stays close to me. I walk down to the pool, I walk to the large grass courtyard where I played football with the boys and fell in love with Brian Manerino shortly after I kicked his ass when he shouted at me.

A year later, I still walk Taffy around. I am walking back from the pool and I see a man sitting on his patio outside of a ground floor apartment. He is wearing a blue bathrobe. He calls my dog over even though he does not know us. She runs to him and he picks her up. He asks me what my name is and through my scowl and doubting eyes, I tell him. He asks me where I live. I nod my head nondescriptively and say, "Over there." He begins talking but I am not listening. Instead, I am watching as he pets Taffy so vigorously that he causes his bathrobe to open and I see his dick. I have never seen a dick before but I know I do not want to be seeing this and I am furious and frightened all at once. I walk over and grab my dog from him. He pulls his robe back together, ties the belt and snickers. I want to punch his mother-fucking face. But I am only nine and I know he could hurt me. I walk as fast as I can back to our apartment.

Still nine, we are playing Truth or Dare. I have been hanging out with Brian, his brother Todd, and their stepsister Doreen all summer. I find out years later that their mother, Pam, and Doreen's father, Ted, were swingers. Pam used to come over to our apartment and have coffee with my mother. They sat at our kitchen table, drank coffee, sometimes wine, smoked cigarettes, and at one point, my mother told me, Pam asked her and George to "join" her and Ted. My mother and I laughed at this.

We are in Doreen's bedroom. Brian and Todd live with their father, but spend the weekends with Pam and Ted and that is when I get to hang out with them. We are on the bottom bunk of bunk beds with a blanket hanging from the top bunk, acting like a curtain. Sharon, Doreen's little sister, is out on the couch with Pam and Ted. We spin the bottle and spread small kisses. Brian and Doreen, Todd and Doreen, Todd and me, Brian and me. Brian is short and has the type of little boy body where underlying muscle pushes out fat, so he is chunky but masculine at the same time. He has dimples under his eyes when he smiles, which is often, and a playful laugh and beautiful curly brown hair. When the bottle points to me, Doreen says, "You have to French kiss Brian." I know that she has a crush on Brian, even though he is her stepbrother, and even though she knows

I love him, so I agree, even though I have never stuck my tongue into a boy's mouth. We do it, but only for a second because Brian has never done it either. His tongue is softer than I had expected, and it tastes like Sweet Tarts. I like it. As I walk home in the dark, I go over the kiss in my head again and again and the butterflies make my stomach ache to the point I think I will fall to the ground.

When I walk into the apartment, I hear my older sister telling my mother that her friend April's rats had babies. We have two black-hooded rats as pets ourselves, Bridget and Bernie, after the characters in a sitcom, and April adores them so she purchased a rat herself. My sisters and I love those rats. We hold them on our shoulders as we watch television. Sometimes on Saturday nights my mother lets us bring our sleeping bags into the family room and sleep on the floor. On those nights, we take out Bridget and Bernie and put them on our heads. They leave turds in our hair, but we don't care. We climb into our sleeping bags and let the rats run around in them, tickling our legs. They leave turds in our sleeping bags, but we don't care. So my sister is telling my mother how April's father was angry about the rat, and even angrier when the rat had babies. He flushed the little furless pink babies down the toilet. For years I will have visions in my head of those tiny creatures, helpless and blind, spinning with the water until they finally followed gravity and disappeared into the sewers. Drown, dead, and floating in piss and shit.

When I wait in the lunch line at school, I wonder why my lunch tickets are blue while the other kids' tickets are yellow. I find out soon enough that I am on the government lunch program when a boy points it out to the other kids in line and laughs at me. This is not the same boy who spits in my ear on the playground after he sees my "pony sized" ten-speed bike because my mother cannot afford a normal ten-speed. I begin to pack my own lunches, often. I make peanut butter and marshmallow cream sandwiches, throw in small bags of Fritos, and wrap cans of pop in aluminum foil so they will stay cold through the morning. It never works, but I like pop so I'm willing to drink it with crackling carbonation seeming wider at room temperature.

I wander alone a lot. After I get home from school, I walk around the complex. Sometimes I walk to downtown Arvada two miles away. Sometimes I only walk to the gas station at the other end of the complex, drop a quarter into the vending machine to get a Dr. Pepper or Bubble Up, then call my mother on the pay phone. She does not believe me when I tell her my older sister is beating me up on a regular basis. My mother thinks I'm exaggerating. Often times, I hide under the bed. My sister has tried to smother me with a pillow. Once, she grabbed the whistling kettle from the stove and forced the boiling water out of it to land onto my chest. I ran screaming into my mother's bedroom. My mother still does not believe that my older sister beats me. Whenever I make these phone calls pleading for her to come home, to stop my sister, to help me, she tells me to go back home and to stop being so dramatic. Years later, my mother will ask my younger sister if it was true. My younger sister will respond, "Yes, it was bad." My older sister never hits my younger sister.

One day while wandering, I stroll around the remains of the once-harvested apple orchard on the edge of our complex. I walk around the trees because I am drawn to them. Their thick, scraggly branches, and tough bark. Their delicate green leaves thriving in summer, hardening in fall, dropping and failing and crumbling by winter. It is still summer and I can see clearly everything on the green lawn before my footsteps. And then I see them. Three tiny dead birds. I think they have fallen out of a nest. I pick one up and I see that there is a blue thumbtack stuck into its chest. I pick up the other two, and they, also, have been stabbed in the chest with tacks. I hold the precious dead beings in the palm of my hand and try to understand what person could do this. It is one more piece to my frantic, puzzled existence and it is then that I know there is no God.

I miss my father. His absence is part of the equation of grimness that is rotting my immature core. When he wasn't yelling at my mother, he was fun. He would play kickball in our yard with the neighbor kids and me; he would give me nickels to massage his socked feet while he lay on the couch. He called me Tiger. I will not understand until much later the dichotomy of a man who can hit his wife and then play with his children, and even then, I'm not sure I completely comprehend or ever will.

My mother never talks about him unless he comes to pick us up, which is rare. He only wants to take my older sister and me. He does not want to deal with my younger sister. She is still in diapers. He tells my mother, while wearing his sunglasses to hide his purple and green swollen eye, that he is going to take us to a movie. We are excited. My mother keeps her arms crossed, still wearing her robe, still smelling of maple syrup after she has made us French toast, my favorite. She is reluctant, I can tell. She lets us go with him and I am not sure if it's because she knows how much we want to spend time with him or if it's because she wants to get rid of us for the day.

We climb into the car and he drives us to the Red Lion Inn. He tells us he is going in to make a phone call. He does not return for three hours and my older sister and I count how many vodka bottles are stashed beneath the front seat. Three. When we see him walking across the parking lot, we scurry into the backseat and he moves his six-foot-two, slender body into the driver's seat, and never says a word. There is no movie. There are no previews to our story, no sweet sodas to sip, salty popcorn to crunch, or chocolaty candies to melt in our mouths. He takes us back home. I don't recall if the car swerved.

Alisa A. Gaston-Linn

Sandy takes her girls and moves out, I don't know where they went, my mother does not tell us, but frankly, I don't care. I don't want to see green boogers anymore or fear that Cathy will let a little girl drown. Chris moves in. He is two and I don't know his mother's name, but she has long, ash-blonde hair, is tall and thin, and does not speak to people. We often play in the hallways of our building, all kids who live there presently. Chris comes to play with my sisters and me and my younger sister's best friend, Charity who is the same age as she. My older sister and I often babysit Charity. Her mother Cindy is a scientist or something similar, and I like her and her funky eyeglasses. I also like their black lab named Cinder. My younger sister and Charity look like twins, both with blonde hair and blue eyes, and precious, petite noses. None of us know what to think of Chris. He is a brat. He wants things his way and often yells at us. But he is two, so we all laugh at him and eventually send him back downstairs to go home. We send him home also when he smells like shit, which is often. His diaper fills and sags and he stinks so we send him home.

It is Saturday and my mother is taking me with her to the grocery store. We open our front door to leave and see that there is thick brown mud wiped all over it. But then we smell it and understand that it is not mud, it is shit. I tell my mother it must be Chris's shit. I don't know anyone else who would have quick and easy access to shit, so much so, he could wipe what seems to be pounds of it across our door. My mother tells me to stay put. She storms downstairs and I hear her pound on Chris's door, Chris's mother opening the door, and my mother keeping calm but using that tone she uses with us when she will use the wooden spoon or belt to spank us, so I know how much trouble Chris's mother is in. My mother walks to the building security door, looks up at me and says, "Let's go."

When we return from the grocery store, the shit is cleaned off our door but the smell lingers. We are walking into our apartment that now has a threshold of feces aroma and I hope it goes away soon because there is no way I'm asking my friends to come over while this threshold remains. Chris and his mother move away shortly after he smeared shit on our door.

I meet Natalie. She is the first black girl I've ever known. Her hair is the most wonderful display of blackness and sheen and fancy braids that I've ever seen and I am immediately envious. I want my long, stringy blonde hair to be stiff and thick and brutal like hers. She is a year younger than me, and her brother, Clay, is in my fifth grade class. Whenever I go over to their apartment, which is a few buildings to the south, we are restricted to play in their bedroom. It smells like piss because Clay wets his bed. This is what Natalie tells me. I feel sorry for Clay. I have to sleep with my little sister, but I don't wet the bed and she doesn't wet the bed and I can't imagine sleeping in a bed saturated with urine because my mother is trying to teach me a lesson.

Natalie and I hang out all through the fall. The apartment complex playground is right next to my building. It has four plastic-board swings on a tall, metal frame, a wooden seesaw, and a merry-go-round. Natalie swings higher than anyone except Doreen. They have contests sometimes. Doreen smiling high up in the air with her wavy, blonde hair in a straight stream, defying gravity, and her buck teeth protruding. Natalie's pigtails stay in place as she swings higher and higher. I try to keep up, but I am afraid to go higher. I will come to know later in life how much fear I have festered within me over the years. They swing higher and higher and sometimes they jump off the swings landing into the sand just before the merry-go-round. I watch them, knowing that I will only jump into the sand when I'm alone because I don't want anyone else to see my pathetic attempt from a low-sailing swing.

Natalie and I often play in the field across from my building. One day we are playing and an argument begins. I think it had to do with where our pretend houses would be. We verbally fight dirty, and I think I'm tough and tell her not to mess with me. But she does. She kicks the shit out of me and I am lying on the ground with dirt all over me and dried up weeds poking me in the face. I cry hard and tell her I'm going to get my older sister, then run into my apartment. This is the only time I can ever remember my older sister protecting me. We walk outside and see Natalie across the playground, across the parking lot, peeking out of her building security door. My older sister shouts, "If you touch her again, I'll kick your ass!"

Natalie yells back, "Fuck you!" And runs into her building. A second later, she pokes her head out again. My older sister begins to walk in her direction so Natalie runs back into her building. We never play together again and soon after our fight, her family moves out of the complex.

Bennie and Timmy move in across the hall from us. Bennie is dreamy. He is my older sister's age, eleven, and he looks like he walked right out of the ocean. I imagine he is a surfer. His white hair wet and water dripping off his tan body as he sails through the waves on a board. His blue eyes are soft and he is sweet. My older sister has a crush on him so there is no way I tell her I have a crush on him as well. Instead, I must tolerate Timmy. Timmy is not dreamy. He looks like The Grinch with slanted eyes and tan skin wrinkled way before its time because he is only my age. His eyes are also blue but they are sinister-looking and his brown hair flaps into his face as he bounces around, barely able to keep his toes on the ground. He has a crush on me, I know this. He follows me around and wants to play all the time and I am forced to play because my older sister wants to be around Bennie. But Timmy is funny. He makes me laugh in all of his awkwardness so I soon learn it's not so bad to be around him. But I don't want to French kiss him.

The four of us are on the playground along with my older sister's friend, Lisa, who is tall and lanky with stringy blonde hair like mine. She is a latchkey kid as well and she wears her keys on a chain around her neck and I think this is dorky. Her single father is raising her. I don't know where her mother is but they are from Des Moines, Iowa so I'm guessing her mother is back there. As we all play on the swings and the merry-go-round, my older sister and Lisa get on the seesaw. It's painted green but the paint is peeling off and we can see the exposed wood. They have a game. Lisa weighs one end of the seesaw down to the ground while my sister slides down toward her. Then they switch. They do this a few times until my older sister screams. She stands up and we see an inch of a thin, piece of wood sticking out of her jeans on her butt.

She and I go inside and she lies on my mother's bed and tells me to pull it out. I grab on and pull as hard as I can but it's not coming. It's not even budging. She yells at me and calls me weak. She tells me to try again. It does not budge. We are sick to our stomachs because we know we have to call our mother at work and she will not be happy. She is not happy when we tell her my sister has a large splinter in her butt cheek. When she gets home, she tries to pull out the extra-large splinter, but again, it does not budge. She helps my sister take off her jeans and her underwear and then tries again. Nothing. So she wraps a blanket around my sister's waist and the three of us pile into the car. She doesn't bother to bring my younger sister who is at Charity's.

At the doctor's office, they give my sister a shot in the butt and she cries out as her long, wavy, thick brown hair falls over her face, and the doctor has to cut out the splinter. When he shows us what was stuck in my sister's butt, we all gasp. No wonder I could not pull it out. It is six-inches long with a diameter about three times the size of a toothpick. My older sister puts it into her scrapbook.

Bennie and Timmy move away and my older sister never gets to French kiss Bennie.

My mother breaks up with George. At first, I don't care because one time I went to the store with George in his red car I would find out much later was a Porsche Targa, and he waited in the car while he sent me in for a few things. It was my first experience with "impulse buying." As I waited in line to pay, I grabbed a small pack of Juicy Fruit and laid it on the counter with the rest of the items. When I got back into the car and gave George his change, he demanded to know why it came up short. I told him I didn't know as my body began to tremble. I felt so incredibly ashamed that I wanted to disappear into the black leather seat fitted so comfortably and firm against my small body. He kept demanding, then he grabbed the receipt out of the bag. He saw the gum listed.

"Did you buy a pack of gum?"

I'm sure my face was the color of the reddest of red mud. "Oh, yeah, that. I forgot."

George smiled at me. "It's okay if you wanted some gum, but you need to tell me if you do something like that." He rubbed the top of my head then we zoomed off in his car.

Even though he was fat, bald, and wore glasses, and my mother was thin, and stylish, and gorgeous, he made us all laugh. He took us to parks in the fall where we rolled in the leaves. He talked to my sisters and me as though he were truly interested in what we had to say. He dumped all of my mother's booze over the balcony one night when he felt she had been drinking too much. I had sat in the dark of my room, listening to their argument, with Barbara Streisand blaring on the stereo, my mother drunk. I was glad. I didn't want my mother to be a drunk like my father. So I am sad to see George go.

Alisa A. Gaston-Linn

Charity and my younger sister are playing in the laundry room of our building. They come running home and tell my older sister and me that a man came into the room and pulled down his pants. They tell us they saw his "wiener." They are only five. We tell them to stay out of the laundry room. A few days later, my little sister and Charity are playing in our kitchen and my sister sticks a pea in her nostril. She and Charity laugh so hard that the pea is sucked up and lodges itself deep into my sister's nose. My older sister and I try to get the pea out by pushing on my younger sister's nose. This time, with things stuck into body parts, we don't call my mother. We call my grandpa. He comes over and as he crouches down to peer into my sister's nose, he does not take off his jean jacket. I look at the faded jacket, and his jeans, and his cowboy boots and he smells like chewing tobacco and Old Spice and I love this man more than anything on this earth because he is not afraid to hug my sisters and me. Each time he leaves us, he kisses us good-bye and tells us he loves us. My mother does not do this. I want to be with my grandpa always, next to him in his big green Ford truck.

He takes a small flashlight out of his front pocket, the kind of light that looks like a pen. The small dart of light searches into the crevasses of my little sister's miniature nose and there we all see it. The pea is in perfect form. My grandpa holds my sister's head, then places his thumb at the top of her nose and presses hard and my sister cries, but he presses still and slowly pushes the pea down. When it's about to drop, he holds up the palm of his hand and the tiny green vegetable, covered in snot, lightly plops into his huge hand. He hugs my sister and tells her to never do anything like that again. She doesn't.

Sometimes after school, I hop on the bus with my best friend, Rachelle. I normally walk home from school, down the path parallel to the busy street where a blue convertible once pulled next to my older sister and me and the man asking us for directions had his dick out. I knew what one looked like by then so I didn't care even though every nerve in my body signaled that this is was not right. My older sister ignored him and shoved me forward to walk. So Rachelle gets to ride the bus home because she lives in a nice neighborhood with large homes and beautiful lawns. My mother has told me that I am not to go anywhere after school unless I call her first and ask. But I ignore this rule often, or I forget, because riding on the bus with Rachelle, and walking into her front door where her mother greets her, and we have snacks that are good for us, and her little white dog, Charlie, follows us and is so soft, is too tempting when I'm standing there at school, watching my best friend get on that bus and she asks me to come along. Each time I call my mother from Rachelle's house, I shake because I know my mother will be livid. She picks me up on the way home from work and yells at me. We never did tell her about the guy in the convertible.

I do eventually tell her about Bill. I am at the playground with Brian and Todd and some other kids I don't know. One of the kid's fathers is there. Some of the kids practice pitching a baseball to one another and hitting it with a red, aluminum bat. I'm watching near the merry-go-round. It happens quickly. The whack rings in my ears at the same moment I see a large object and then feel incredible pain in my eye. I cover my eye and cry, I bend over. The father walks up to me, crouches down and tries to pull my hand away, but I fight him. He is nice and reassuring and he calms me down and when he pulls my hand away, every kid on the playground says, "Whoa!" My friend Brian tells me later that they all saw my eye swell up.

My friends walk me to my apartment and my mom is there because it's Saturday. She pulls me into the bathroom, looks at my eye, then brings an icepack from the kitchen. She walks me to the family room and sits me down on the couch and says, "What kind of idiot let's kids play baseball in that tiny playground?"

She tells me I can stay home from school until my eye goes down a bit. It turns spectacular hues of purple, green, and blue. It remains swollen for several days. She goes to work and I lie on the couch and watch television. My mother comes home and hands me a small, stuffed lamb with a black face. She laughs hysterically. I am thrilled because she bought me a gift, but I am also humiliated. I realize how blackened my eye is and don't want to go to school until I look the way I used to look.

On the third day, Bill calls. I am in my bathrobe and it is morning. He asks me if my mother is home. I tell him she's at work. He says he's a friend of hers but I can't recall meeting him. He calls me every day and he is interested in knowing what I think about things and how I like school. He asks me if I have ever seen two dogs on top of each other. I think this is an odd question and imagine the dogs I've seen in the apartment complex playing together, so I answer, "yes." He asks me what I think about it. I tell him, "I don't know."

The next day Bill calls me again and I am excited. I have been looking forward to his call. He sounds lovely over the phone and I like talking because I've been so alone for so long. Then he asks me if I would like to sit on his lap sometime. I don't understand this question so I say, "I don't know," and blush a bit. Then he whispers something I can't quite understand so I ask him to repeat it. He does but I think I've heard him wrong because I don't think he would say something like this to me so I ask him again and he says louder, "I want to suck your tits."

I hang up immediately and I am quivering so uncontrollably I have to go lie down. When my mother comes home, I tell her that her friend Bill called. She says, "Bill? I don't have a friend named Bill." I tell her everything and she yells at me and says she told me not to answer the door while I was alone. I tell her, "But you didn't tell me not to answer the phone."

My mother tells my father he is no longer allowed to pick us up and take us for the day. He has shown up drunk, or gotten drunk too many times while we waited in the car. A few years later, when I am in junior high, he will show up at my junior high school, drunk, and try to take me. The principal of the school will go out into the parking lot and confront my father. I, as well as many other students, will watch through the windows of the common area while my father waves his hands and the principal calms him down. I will call my mom who will send her boyfriend, Hal, to the school. Hal will talk to my dad in the parking lot for a long time until my dad finally leaves. My older sister will be enraged because my father won't ask for her. He will only ask for me. She remembers it differently.

We will never see my father again, until I am in my late twenties and he has been homeless on the streets of Denver for ten years, and he has difficulty remembering who my sisters and I are when we visit him in the hospital after he was found on the sidewalk having a seizure. He dies several years later when I am thirty-three with no memory of my mother or us.

Hal begins dating my mother when I am nine, and by the time I am ten, he spends more and more time at our shitty apartment, only he does not spend time with the collective us, he spends time only with my mother. He does not speak to my sisters and me unless my mother is punishing us and he feels the need to insert his power. Like the time in seventh grade when my best friend, Becky, and I lie to our parents about spending the night at each other's homes and instead spend the night at a park party with about thirty other kids from school. We watch kids get drunk and puke and we run and hide from the cops. I kiss Grant Pratt only to find out the next week at school that not only does he not want to be my boyfriend, but he does not even know my name.

Hal yells at us when my mother needs backup, ignores us the rest of the time, and spends the night in my mother's bed. They lock the door. When I have my chronic nightmares and call out to my mother, she yells at me to "get up and get a glass of water then go to bed!" She does not open the door. But a few times, she does. When Hal stays at his bachelor pad, and I have my nightmares and she becomes my mother again. She invites me into her bed and I fall asleep next to her. I am immediately soothed by her clean smell, by the softness of her sheets. I wake when her alarm clock goes off playing songs like I Can See Clearly Now by Johnny Nash, and Close to You by The Carpenters. But my mother tells me to sleep as she takes a shower and drinks her coffee while putting on her makeup. These are the best nights and mornings of my life.

I wake up one Saturday morning to find Hal at our breakfast table. He smiles at me as my mother says nothing but it is clear to me he's moving in with us. I do not make any attempt to hide the scowl on my face. I don't eat the pancakes my mother has set before me. I watch him drink his coffee and smoke his cigarette and I hate him.

My anger swells like my eye had swollen that time on the playground. Over the next several years my anger settles and stays and does what my body had done when the cells around my eye filled with fluid to protect my damaged tissue. My anger protects me from further damage by cushioning the area.

When I am 14, mom and Hal buy a house. We move from apartment 135 and I never look back. My mother works her way up to vice president of the insurance brokerage, I go to a brand new junior high school where very few people know me. My old junior high and another junior high merged certain students from certain zip codes and now we all attend the new junior high with chemically saturated carpet that tricks us because it smells new and fresh. No one here knows I came from misery. The friends who had come to the apartment to play with me stayed in the old junior high. So I can begin again. I can pretend that I have grown up in a gorgeous middle class home like the rest of the students. I can pretend that my dad is not a homeless drunk and that my older sister has not left scars. I can pretend that my mother is happy to have us. I can leave my old existence behind in the old carpet, the carpet that festers with the stench of broken, sad families trying to survive. I can pretend it never happened.

I am decades older now. I am married and have a little girl. I have a large home that looks across protected space where elk come down from Rocky Mountain National Park, and the owls woo us at night, and the same pack of coyotes makes its rounds on summer nights walking from the open space, around our neighborhood, down to the lake, then back into the open space. A mountain lion was spotted near our mailboxes the other day. I live roughly twenty-five miles from the shitty apartment complex.

Much forgiveness envelops our family. My older sister has made amends and she has been an amazing mother to her son and daughter who are both at university. My mother has apologized for the inattention, for the lack of warmth. We have fought it out, come together, and are now extremely close. She is a loving, affectionate "Nana" to all of her grandchildren. I understand now the pressure and angst that cloaked my mother while we were in apartment 135. I can comprehend my older sister's anger and her need for an outlet. Hal has reflected on the impact of his neglect, and has sought forgiveness from my sisters and me. Yet only my older sister and I share the redemption because long ago my younger sister chose the dance with heroin and has long since been in that malignant ballroom. My mother is raising my nine-year-old nephew and after my younger sister's many bouts in jail and rehab, we no longer know her whereabouts. I am overwhelmed with sorrow over her path that so closely mirrors my father's. I miss her. I miss my grandpa who stuck by three little girls until they grew into adults and he died of cancer. We don't spend much time with my grandma who lives in a retirement community.

My mother and Hal are now well off. My older sister and her husband, and my husband and I, are upper middle class. I have traveled to numerous countries, I have given myself to causes, and great friends surround me. Most important, I am capable of much love, especially toward my child. But the germs remain. No amount of money or curing can help me escape the memory of the vulgar environment that shaped my internal landscape.

When I must drive through that small city where the apartment complex sits, I take out-of-the-way streets. I have a friend who lives in a pleasant neighborhood that was built down the road from the complex long after we had moved out. When I go to her house, I never drive south of her neighborhood. I never reach the crossroads that corner the buildings of my childhood.

As I have moved through life, I have packed the swollen ire with ice. It has gone down, the tissue has repaired itself, but I feel the residual damage beneath. That apartment complex was like a broken centrifuge, failing to separate the good from the evil, mixing all of us in a concentrated square of buildings and leaving children with the inability to distinguish themselves from the contemptible. I continue to fight the feeling that I am not laudable. I continue to fight the germs. I am afraid that even with my nice clothes, and fancy shoes, and clean makeup, and free-flowing curls, as I sip red wine at literary parties, people will know that I do not belong. Unless I can keep the bacteria that is forever on me contained.

Alisa A. Gaston-Linn

Sometimes I wonder if I should show my husband where I grew up, or if when my little girl is older, I should show her, but then reality shifts. If I venture too close, go back to that apartment complex, to apartment 135, the bacteria will grow, the microorganisms encompassing my human flora, and it will suffocate me with its pathogenic scheme. I am not that place, I tell myself. But the existence of that place has formed onto me, my flowing cells, my consciousness, my skin and hair and eyelashes. So I try to remain sanitized. I will not go back.

Alisa A. Gaston-Linn

THE SCOW

Elaine Ford

I hold in my hand two metal disks. Each has a seven-digit number stamped on one side and a hole drilled in the edge. Dulled with corrosion or ash, they look as if they have passed through fire, and I guess that's true. Gritty dust rubs off on my fingers.

This is what's left of them. My parents: John and Ella Hopkin, longtime residents of 23 Hillside Terrace, Brookfield, New Jersey, dead and gone these thirty years.

In some ways, it's fitting that these humble pieces of metal, which I have come upon in a box of odds and ends in my desk, are almost the only physical remnants of their lives. They would have disapproved of gravestones, resisted the idea of brass plaques. They disliked fuss, both of them.

Their reticence was partly on account of their upbringing: You don't whine in public, nor do you exult. Even within the family you don't speak of pain. Or grief.

But it's also a fact that they reached adulthood during the Depression, when people had to hoard every resource. For my parents, I think, the habit of thrift somehow came to include their store of feelings. Even if they had been religious, the concept of a funeral, especially one involving a casket surrounded by weeping mourners, would have struck them as profligate, both of money and of emotional energy.

That's why they joined the burial society, the function of which was to deal with a dead body as cheaply and expeditiously as possible—in their case, by cremation. They didn't consult with me, their only child, about this decision: They probably assumed that what was going to happen to their earthly remains was none of my business. At the time they signed up with the society they were actuarily far from death, and I was absorbed in gestating my first child. Even if they'd informed me, I doubt I would have given their decision a second thought

But lives do not always conform to actuarial tables. One Sunday afternoon not many years later, as I was folding clothes in the laundry room, the phone rang in the kitchen. "Something happened to your mother," Dad said.

"What? What happened?"

"She fell down the cellar steps."

In my mind's eye I saw those steps. Narrow, splintered, cluttered with muddy work boots and cans of bent nails, saved from total darkness by a single 25-watt bulb.

I gripped the edge of the counter. "Is she going to be all right?"

"No, Franny. She's gone."

Gone? Just like that?

There would be no funeral, my dad told me. No memorial service, either. "That's the way she wanted it."

Before her body was cold, practically, the burial society spirited it off.

Two weeks later, when Carl had returned from a business trip and could mind the kids, I drove down to New Jersey, to the house I'd grown up in—the five-room bungalow that my parents paid four thousand dollars for in 1939. All over again I was surprised at how small and cramped and jam-packed the rooms were. And how frigid, since the thermostat was invariably set at sixty-two degrees.

At my dad's request I went through Mom's jewelry, choosing a few pieces to keep, and bagged up her clothes to give away. What set me to weeping was a cotton housecoat, red piping on the collar and cuffs, geraniums faded to pink, a rip in the threadbare cloth below the pocket mended with tiny even stitches. In one of the earliest photos of me my mother wears that housecoat. I am a naked, bemused, round-faced infant; she is girlish, even pretty. I considered cutting off the square red buttons and saving them to sew on another garment, but taking scissors to the housecoat seemed too violent an act. Maybe some customer of the Salvation Army would do it. I couldn't. I folded the housecoat into the plastic garbage bag with everything else.

For dinner I made fish chowder, my father's favorite. As I stood at the stove stirring the soup so it wouldn't stick to the bottom of the dented old kettle, my father looked into the pot. At my elbow he gave off a strong odor of pipe tobacco, shreds of which adhered to his plaid wool shirt, and bay rum. Maybe, I thought, he was comparing the thickness of the chowder to my mother's. Suddenly, clumsily, he embraced me. "Oh, Franny," he said with a croak. Then he let me go and blew his nose hard. Even now, three decades later, I can't eat fish chowder without experiencing again that brief moment when my father revealed to me his sorrow.

It took some courage to ask him what had become of my mother's ashes. He might well have told the burial society to dispose of them as they saw fit.

"Hall closet shelf," he answered.

I tried to talk him into a little private ceremony. "You and I can go somewhere nice, and scatter them," I said. "Like the duck pond." Maybe read a few poems: Ever since I could remember there'd been a volume of Edna St.Vincent Millay in the front-room bookcase.

My dad looked at me as if I'd lost my mind. "The *duck* pond?"

To be sure, in the years since I'd graduated from high school and left home the duck pond had become encroached upon by an industrial park composed of prefab metal structures and the new multipurpose municipal building, also prefab.

"Well, you choose a spot, then."

He just shrugged. In the end, I had to return to Belmont without having managed any kind of ceremony to memorialize my mother.

The following February, on a Sunday morning almost exactly a year after her death, my father's car slid into a concrete barrier next to road construction on Route 4. Uncharacteristically, he wasn't wearing a seat belt, and according to the state trooper who called to give me the news, he'd been doing at least seventy when the car hit the black ice. "Route 4?" I said to Carl after I hung up. An endless strip of crummy stores some distance from where my dad lived: discount warehouses with names like Crazy Harry's, muffler shops, unfinished-furniture outlets. "What could he have needed so desperately?" I wailed. "On Route 4? On a Sunday morning?"

Once again, no body for me to grieve over. Once again, "No public service, at his request"—a request spelled out in the terse obituary he'd written for himself and deposited with the burial society. All that remained for me to do was empty out the house so it could be sold.

Because of the kids, I couldn't just take off on a moment's notice. And I admit I wasn't eager to face the accumulation of my parents' thirty years in that house. So it was June before I finally went down to do the job.

Before I left Belmont, I'd ordered up by phone a Dumpster from a local waste disposal company. "The biggest one you've got," I'd said to the woman down in Hackensack, on the other end of the line. Sure enough, there it sat, plonked in the driveway next to the house, a veritable scow that might just have returned from a garbage-dumping voyage to Malaysia, a scabrous insult to the eye in this modestly respectable suburban neighborhood. On tiptoes I peered over the side. The rusted interior was empty except for some sodden sheaves of newspaper.

With the key that I took from the fake rock beside the stoop, I unlocked the kitchen door. The house, which had been closed up for four months, smelled of mold, pipe smoke, and something vaguely sweet and rotten, as though a piece of fruit had fallen behind the refrigerator. My shoes stuck to dirty linoleum.

I got down a glass from the cupboard and turned on the tap. Brackish water sputtered from the faucet. Hoping for root beer or ginger ale, I looked inside the refrigerator. Nothing like that. All the real perishables were gone, too, probably disposed of by the next-door neighbors, who also had access to the key so they could keep an eye on the place. What remained were pickles and mustard, a can of Maxwell House, the jar of gourmet strawberry preserves I'd given him for Christmas. I unscrewed the lid. One teaspoon scooped out, the rest crystallized. Didn't he like it? Or had he only just opened it before the accident? My eyes began to tear.

That night, after a supper of freezer-burned toast and peanut butter and a shot of my dad's Canadian Club, I slept in my own childhood bed. The sheets that I'd taken from the linen closet still gave off the scent of Sweetheart soap, the oval cakes of which my mother used to remove from their boxes and leave as fresheners on the shelves. I wasn't sure that brand of soap was on the market anymore.

Sometime during the night I was awakened by thunder. Rain crashed against the window glass. I remembered the summer that cracks appeared in my bedroom ceiling and rainwater dripped onto the rug, and when my father climbed a ladder to patch the shingles, he slipped off the roof and scared the wits out of me (and probably my mother too although she didn't show it) but by a miracle broke no bones.

I remembered how my cat Timmy used to hide under my bed during thunderstorms, imagining he could keep himself safe that way. I realized I had never slept alone in this house before.

The next morning I stood at the kitchen counter and ate more toast, this time with my Dad's hard-as-rock preserves instead of peanut butter. I gazed out at the backyard, in which knee-high grass grew, gone to seed. Because all spring I'd kept saying to Carl, "next week I'll try to go down," or "definitely, the week after," we'd never hired someone to keep the lawn mowed. At the rear of the yard, beneath some discouraged Rose of Sharon bushes, were stacks of windows that my dad scavenged some years back, when they tore down the old town hall. He'd talked about maybe building a greenhouse when he retired. At first the windows had been covered by a tarp, but it must have blown off in a storm. Some of the panes were broken, and dandelions sprouted through the gaps in the glass.

Depression Mentality, I've heard it called, the pathological impulse to accumulate bargains and freebies, linked with the inability to throw anything away. Nobody suffered from the disorder worse than my parents. You don't replace something perfectly serviceable simply because it's unattractive or not in the best condition, and when it breaks down or falls apart altogether, you put it in the cellar, because you might get around to fixing it sometime. You never know when that piece of scrap plywood or odd-sized pan lid will come in handy. In some ways I sympathized. They'd lived through lean years. His ambitions for higher education thwarted, my father took a low-paying clerical job after high school, and perhaps out of discouragement, he remained stuck in it. My mother earned pin money by doing demeaning little tasks like running up the costumes for a neighbor child's dance recital on her balky old Singer. Their nutty ways had roots in genuine experience.

I was determined, however, not to take on the burden of their possessions. This was 1970, when I and my contemporaries believed in traveling light, gathering no moss. Even the husband and two kids I'd acquired seemed like considerable baggage to my college roommates, one of whom was a photojournalist, constantly on the road, and the other a Foreign Service officer stationed in Istanbul. Hence the Dumpster in the driveway, hence my plan to make a quick, surgical strike. I would allot no more than three days to this operation.

Since I was standing in the kitchen, toast in hand, I decided to start right there. I began to pull things out of cupboards and separate them into two piles: the cookware and appliances destined for the Salvation Army and the useless junk that no one could possibly want. The latter pile quickly became the largest. By nine o'clock the temperature in the house was in the high humid eighties; my parents had never seen the need for air conditioners. A hot breeze, laden with grass pollen, moved the café curtains in the open window. As I worked I occasionally became aware of the strange sweet-rotten odor I'd noticed the day before. The smell wasn't exactly unpleasant. Mystifying is more the word. For company I tried to tune in WQXR on my mother's counter top radio. All I could get without static was mindless jabber on WOR.

Devoutly I wished I had not ventured upon this job alone. I should have left the kids with friends and dragged Carl down here to help. At least he would have been somebody to laugh with over the insane objects I found squirreled away in the backs of drawers: bundles of milk bottle wires from the forties; thousands of rubber bands; half clothespins missing their springs; bags and bags of rags; those little plastic covers like shower caps that my mother once put over dishes of leftovers, now disintegrating and useless; partly-burnt birthday candles and pencil stubs and ball-point pens that no longer wrote. I emptied shelves full of ugly, mismatched china, mostly the former possessions of various deceased relatives, gadgets that no longer worked, washed mayonnaise jars, and on and on and on. Part of me felt the fascination of an archeologist in this midden heap, this palpable record of the domestic culture of the early twentieth century. A bigger part of me felt disgust at my parents' insecurity, their compulsive need to save all this rubbish against some future disaster.

The discards I carried out to the scow, many armloads full, and pitched over the side. I cringed as crockery smashed against metal. I felt especially bad about a set my mother had served iced tea in: tall blue-green china mugs with wooden handles, and a matching pitcher. Maybe they'd been a wedding present. However, only one mug remained intact, and the pitcher's lip was chipped and a black fissure ran up the side. I didn't enjoy throwing them away, but I couldn't rescue every single object to which some memory still clung, could I?

"Oh, she was hard," you might well say about my twenty-eight-year-old self. To be honest, I'd do the job differently now.

Next I attacked the front room. All the furniture, and there was a lot of it for a room that measured no more than twelve by fourteen, would go to the Salvation Army. Into the scow went my father's collection of stinking pipes, a hassock from which kapok had begun to emerge, a cheaply framed print of Van Gogh's sunflowers whose removal left behind a bright rectangle of lords and ladies and feathery trees and horse-drawn carriages on the otherwise faded beige wallpaper, and a floor lamp that had worked only iffily, something wrong with its wiring. I think the lamp was one of the furnishings my parents took possession of when my grandmother died, or perhaps a great uncle had passed it on to them.

Picking through the books, I opened the volume of Millay poems. It had never occurred to me to look inside it before, although as a child I was a great reader. Maybe the old-fashioned binding put me off, or the fact that it was wedged between *A Study of History* by Toynbee and *Decline of the West.* Ella Alice Field—my mother's maiden name—and the date 1928 were written inside the cover in fading green ink, in a more florid and flowing style than she later used, but recognizably her handwriting. She would have been eighteen.

I riffled through the pages and found a stanza my mother had underlined in the same green ink:

My candle burns at both ends;
It will not last the night;
But, ah, my foes, and, oh, my friends—
It gives a lovely light.

I was startled at the thought of my practical, tightlipped mother contemplating burning one's candle at both ends. But that had been in her youth, before the Depression and marriage to my dad. I closed the book and put it in the pile for the town library.

In the afternoon, the next-door neighbor, Mrs. Haas, still in her church dress, came to the kitchen door bearing a small square box. "We're awful sorry about your dad," she said. I wondered if she realized she was, in fact, holding his earthly remains. When the box from the burial society was delivered she'd signed for it and kept it for my arrival.

"So unfortunate," she continued, "those two terrible accidents, one right after the other. You never know what life has in store, do you?"

"No, you never do."

Elaine Ford

Mrs. Haas was a woman in her late sixties whose passion in life, according to my mother, was raising funds to have stray cats neutered and placed in good homes. Since she and her husband had bought the house after I'd grown up and left, I didn't know them very well.

"Lovely people, your mom and dad." Mrs. Haas glanced behind her at the scow, out of which protruded my grandmother's lamp, the shade drunkenly atilt. "Kept to themselves pretty much," Mrs. Haas said, "not that there's anything wrong with that."

I thanked her and took the box.

"Too bad there wasn't some kind of a service. Seems like there's something missing when there isn't a service."

Sweat trickled down my back, under my T-shirt. "Well, that's how they wanted it."

"You have to let people do things their own way, don't you?"

Even when what they insist on doing is wrong-headed, Mrs. Haas meant, but was tactful enough not to say. She looked worried. In her mind was, perhaps, the idea that if you haven't had a funeral, God might not notice that you had died, and you could find yourself drifting in limbo for the rest of eternity. I wasn't sure that I didn't, on some level, suspect the same thing myself.

Mrs. Haas urged me to call on her if I needed anything, anything at all, and turned and stepped off the stoop. Through the screen door I watched her give the scow a wide berth, averting her eyes from the jumble inside, and then cut through a break in the scraggly hedge.

Even with all the windows open, and an electric fan turning fitfully in the dining room window, the curious sweet-rotten smell persisted. Wearily I went out to my car and retrieved the flashlight from the glove compartment. I climbed up onto the kitchen counter and shone it behind the refrigerator, but all I found was dust.

The final room was my parents' bedroom. It was as my father left it that February morning when he took it into his head to drive to Route 4. Blinds shut, closet door slightly ajar, a pair of suspenders dangling from the knob. The covers on his side of the bed were turned back, narrowly; my mother's side remained smoothly tucked in. Sleeping alone, he hadn't moved his body into her space, not so much as an inch. I wasn't sure what to make of his reticence. Did it convey the continuing presence for him of my mother's slight, knobby body, even in death? Or only the meagerness of his sense of self? Either way, the sight made me miserable. I bundled up the sour bedclothes and carried them out to the scow.

Frantic by now to get the ordeal over with, I dealt with the bedroom savagely, refusing to consider who might get some use out of those shoe trees or take pleasure in that tarnished tie clasp, whether any life was left in the dresser scarves or curtains. Everything got tossed. It pained me that so little in this room, this intimate room I'd almost never entered as a child, was worth saving. The pain was physical, like a blow to the chest.

Finally, in early evening, I telephoned Carl. "How's it going?" he asked.

My parents' daughter, I couldn't bring myself to complain. "Not too bad."

"Still think you'll be home Tuesday?" He'd taken two days off work, and the office was short-handed.

"There's the cellar, that's what I'm really dreading. And I have to go through the papers in Dad's desk." The fan on the windowsill began to clank ominously. "They're coming to take away the scow first thing Tuesday morning."

"Scow?"

How ecstatic I would be to see the last of that thing, and all of its depressing, hideous contents. I pictured myself on Tuesday morning, dancing a jig in the road as the scow rattled and groaned down Hillside Terrace.

"Take your time, Fran," Carl said. "Everything's under control here. By the way, I can't find any underwear for Chrissy. Does she have underwear?"

Numb with fatigue, I went into town for something to eat. After my slice of pizza I took the long way back, abandoning four cartons of books on the library steps, hastily, as if the boxes held litters of kittens. I drove around by the duck pond. Teenagers hung out on the bank, probably passing a joint. Green scum floated listlessly on the surface of the water. Nary a duck in sight.

The cellar was where my mother died. Tripped, no doubt, over some piece of junk on the steps, lost her balance, split open her skull on the cement floor. I hadn't been down there since her death, but now I had no choice.

I opened the door and switched on the light. The steps were bare now, perhaps cleared by my father, perhaps by the emergency crew. I paused at the top. I knew what awaited me: electric drills with frayed cords, defunct toasters and shavers and clocks and radios from many eras, cans of dried-out paint, used car batteries and stacks of tires, dozens of dusty Ball canning jars. . . And blood on the floor. I doubted that you could scrub blood out of rough concrete, not with a ton of elbow grease.

Elbow grease. I can't ever get all the grime off the woodwork, no matter how hard I rub. My mother tips the ammonia bottle into my bucket. The fumes make me feel like I'm going to faint. She tells me to quit whining and to use more elbow grease. Idle hands are the devil's tools, she says, not that she believes in the devil.

My mother believes in cod-liver oil, never mind that it makes me gag. She believes in woolen leggings, never mind that my friends all wear dresses to school and have bare legs in January and never once catch pneumonia, never mind that the wool itches like crazy, worse than poison ivy. She believes in shoes with good support (Mary Janes will make your arches fall, like London Bridge) and oatmeal for breakfast and whole-wheat bread because white bread makes your teeth rot and your complexion pasty and three big glasses of milk every day because otherwise you'll get rickets, and never ever Coke, if you drink Coke your teeth will rot *for sure* and fall right out of your head.

My father believes in getting your homework done before dinner in case you get a stomach ache afterward. He believes in riding your bike facing traffic so you can see what's about to hit you and veer off into the ditch. He believes in minding your *p*s and *q*s, minding your own business, minding what you say and do in public because your words and deeds might come back to haunt you.

Always afraid of what might happen, the both of them. Always trying to ward off disaster. And now look what did happen, in spite of all their worrying.

No blood at the bottom of the steps, or none that anyone could see in the puny light of a 25-watter.

I spent most of Monday hauling rubbish up those steps and pitching it over the side of the scow. Every once in a while, after a particularly loud crash, I'd notice Mr. or Mrs. Haas at an upstairs window in their house, staring down on me. They, too, had lived through the Depression. Perhaps they thought that my prodigal wastefulness was inviting the displeasure of God, even more troubling than my parents' unceremonial way of dying.

At half past four the Salvation Army truck arrived. I confess it was hard to watch some of the furniture carried out the door, like the bookcase my father made for me when I was five or six, which was first painted red and later yellow to match daisy wallpaper he put up in my room for my eleventh birthday. But mostly I was happy to see the stuff go.

Again I drove to town for a meal, but this time I didn't go by the duck pond. When I returned, I noticed that my grandmother's floor lamp was no longer in the scow.

The bottle of Canadian Club at my elbow, I sat in the middle of the empty front-room floor and began to go through the papers from Dad's desk. Ancient checkbooks, phone and electricity and gas company receipts from the fifties and sixties. Income tax records. Auto, homeowner's, life insurance policies. Letters and Christmas cards in packets kept together with rubber bands. Mortgage payment stubs going back to the beginning. They'd finally paid the mortgage off last year: I remembered my mother telling me that on the phone, a hint of satisfaction in her voice. It was a few weeks before she fell down the steps.

Then I came to a business-sized envelope addressed to my mother, with a return address from North Bergen Oncology Associates. I pulled out a letter typed on crisp bond paper. "This is to summarize the conversation held in my office on 11/18/68," the doctor wrote. "Liver biopsy confirms a diagnosis of hepatocellular carcinoma."

I knew enough from my one summer as a candy-striper in the county hospital to understand that "hepatocellular carcinoma" meant cancer. Some dreadful kind of cancer.

"At present no drugs are available to treat this condition. Surgery is a possibility in selected cases. Unfortunately, you do not fit that profile. . . We recommend that you continue palliative therapy under the care of your general practitioner. . ."

I couldn't believe it. My mother had shared this information with my father, but not with me. Private she certainly was, a person whose whole philosophy of life prevented her from complaining, yet she was dying of a vicious incurable disease and chose not tell her only child.

Did she suppose she was protecting me, or what?

Angrily I unscrewed the cap on the whisky bottle and took a big swallow.

Why hadn't they sought a second opinion? Or demanded aggressive surgery? Or explored experimental treatments?

But those options would have been expensive, would have called attention to themselves. I began to think of the cellar steps. How much better than an embarrassingly public wasting away would be a headlong leap onto cement. She'd spare my father, spare me, the sight of her gradual decay. Yes, I could believe it of her, the determination such an act would require.

And then I thought of my father's death, almost on the anniversary of hers. Sliding into a concrete wall, going very fast, not buckled in. An unlikely death for him, I'd believed that from the beginning. And, when I thought about it, so like my mother's: its true drama disguised, kept secret from emergency crews, police, coroners, me.

Secrets. I remembered the bloody gauze bundle I saw on the edge of the tub when I got up to pee one morning. I must have been six or seven. "What's that?" I asked, frightened, but my mother just took it away. I remembered the scary red rubber syringe I sometimes found on the toilet tank. For enemas? For other adult purposes I couldn't even guess at? Then there was the time my cat suddenly disappeared. "Where's Timmy?" I demanded to know. "Timmy was sick." "Couldn't the doctor fix him?" "No. Eat your egg."

Were my parents' deaths yet more evidence of their secretiveness, their timidity, their fear of life? Or had they instead, for one time only, when it really counted, looked fate square in the eye and taken control of it?

I got up and went into the dining room to call Carl. The phone sat on the floor now that the rickety wrought iron stand that had held it had gone off to the Salvation Army. I picked up the receiver and heard silence. For a moment I almost panicked. And then it came to me that the phone company had disconnected the line, just as I'd asked them to.

At 8 a.m. Tuesday morning Julio and Miguel from Total Waste Services of Hackensack maneuvered the scow onto a flatbed truck. Standing in the driveway, I watched it rumble down the street and disappear around the corner. I didn't feel ecstasy, or even relief, but rather a sort of dull unease. I rolled up my sleeping bag and stowed it in the car, with cartons of photos and some of my parents' personal effects and papers. A representative from Garden State Realty would look the place over later in the day, but I didn't need to wait for her. She'd let me know over the telephone what the house might sell for.

On the kitchen counter, side by side, remained the two small square boxes containing my parents' ashes. I carried them out into the backyard, along with the Swiss Army knife from my key ring, and knelt under the apple tree my father planted their first summer here. Dew seeped through the knees of my jeans as I slit open the tape sealing the boxes. Inside each was a plastic bag, wired shut at the neck, with a metal identification tag attached. I cut the tags off and poked them into my pocket. Then, one at a time, I up-ended the bags and shook them, letting the breeze carry the ashes into wet, overgrown grass. I didn't say a prayer. I couldn't think of one that would accurately convey my feelings to a God they didn't believe in.

Even then, kneeling there in the backyard, I knew that I hadn't come anywhere close to getting rid of that scow. Its ghost would sail in my wake forever.

About the Authors

Jane Andrews, Raleigh, NC

Jane Andrews has a BA in English from NC State University. Andrews teaches writing and poetry courses through Duke Continuing Education. She is Nonfiction Editor for *The Main Street Rag,* and chair of the Writing Curriculum Committee at OLLI at Duke. Andrews's fiction, essays, memoir and poetry have appeared in *Prime Number Magazine, Red Clay Review, The Dead Mule School of Southern Literature, Verdad Magazine, Kindred, The News and Observer,* and other publications. She is a past board member of Carolina Wren Press and the NC Poetry Society. Andrews is a freelance writing instructor, workshop facilitator, and book editor.

Pam Baggett, Cedar Grove, NC

Pam Baggett's poems appear in *The Atlanta Review, Crab Orchard Review, The Sow's Ear, Kakalak 2014* anthology, the Barefoot Muse Press anthology *Forgetting Home: Poems About Alzheimers,* and *The Southern Poetry Anthology, Volume VII: North Carolina.* A freelance writer and life-long horticulturalist, she is the author/photographer of the garden book *¡Tropicalismo! Spice Up Your Garden with Cannas, Bananas, and 93 Other Eye-Catching Tropical Plants.* Adolescence, rock and roll, the deaths of beloved friends and relatives, and her mother's advancing dementia are themes she currently explores in the sun-filled writing studio she built with a friend a few years ago.

Jessica Barksdale, Pleasant Hill, CA

Jessica Barksdale is the author of thirteen traditionally published novels, including *Her Daughter's Eyes* and *When You Believe.* Her latest, *How to Bake a Man* (Ghostwoods Books, 2014). A Pushcart Prize nominee, her short stories, poems, and essays have appeared in or are forthcoming in *Compose, Salt Hill Journal, The Coachella Review, Carve Magazine, Storyacious, Mason's Road,* and *So to Speak*. She is a professor of English at Diablo Valley College in Pleasant Hill, California, and teaches online novel writing for UCLA Extension.

Arthur Carey, Fremont, CA

Arthur Carey is a former newspaper reporter, editor, and journalism instructor who lives in the San Francisco Bay area. He is a member of the California Writers Club. His fiction has appeared in print and Internet publications, including *The Pedestal, Funny Times, Kind of a Hurricane Press, Eclectic Flash, Writers' Journal, Whortleberry Press, Suspense*, and *Clever Magazine*. His short stories, novel, and a novella, are available on Amazon.com.

Gayle Compton, Virgie, KY

Gayle Compton, a hillbilly from Eastern Kentucky, lives up the creek from where Randall McCoy is buried, and attended college on the hill where "Cotton Top" Mounts was hanged. With deep affection, he tells the story of Appalachia's common people, allowing them to speak, without apology, in their own colorful language. His prize-winning stories, poems and essays have been published in numerous literary journals and anthologies, including *The Kentucky Anthology: Two Hundred Years of Writing in the Blue Grass State, Sow's Ear, Appalachian Heritage, New Southerner,* and *The Blue Collar Review*. His finished poetry and short story collections are seeking a publisher bold enough to confront the Appalachian stereotype.

Beth Copeland, Gibson, NC

Beth Copeland's second poetry collection *Transcendental Telemarketer* (BlazeVOX books, 2012) was runner up in the North Carolina Poetry Council's 2013 Oscar Arnold Young Award for North Carolina's best book of poetry. Her first book *Traveling through Glass* received the 1999 Bright Hill Press Poetry Book Award. Copeland is an Assistant Professor of English at Methodist University. She lives with her husband Phil Rech in a log cabin in Gibson, North Carolina.

J.D. Cortese, Durham, NC

J.D. Cortese is a scientist and educator by training, and a writer out of a passion to communicate. He taught at the University of North Carolina (UNC School of Medicine) and chaired sciences at Durham Technical Community College. He has also written regularly for a widely-read science newspaper, *The Scientist,* served as the at-large editor for the *Human Anatomy and Physiology Society* (HAPS Educator), and as a reviewer for McGraw-Hill and

Prentice Hall. He writes science fiction stories and has recently completed a space-epic novel. But having lived abroad in Argentina and China and also traveled all over the world, earthly places sometimes appear in his writing. Above all habitats, he and his itinerant wife love North Carolina and have been long-time residents of Durham, although his two children (Duke and UNC graduates) remain closer to New York.

Jackie Craven, Schenectady, NY

Jackie Craven has poems published or forthcoming in *The Asheville Poetry Review, Chautauqua, The Fourth River, Nimrod International Journal, Pembroke Magazine, Quiddity, Stone Canoe Journal, Water~Stone Review,* and other journals. After completing her Doctor of Arts in Writing from the University at Albany, she worked for many years as a journalist covering architecture, design, and cultural travel for various publications. Her nonfiction books are *The Healthy Home* and *The Stress-Free Home* (Rockport Publishers). Jackie now divides her time between Florida and upstate New York, where she fixes old houses and rents to interesting people who feed her muse. Visit her at JackieCraven.com.

Paul C. Dalmas, Berkeley, CA

Emerging writer that he imagines himself to be, Paul C. Dalmas spends too much time polishing a hip and eccentric bio to use if he is published. You know: a boyhood selling newspapers on rough city streets, teen years earning minimum wage in the oppressively hot kitchen of a greasy diner, and an adult life working as a boilermaker, helping the poor in Africa, and traveling to Rangiroa, Rajasthan and Rio. In fact, he is a retired high school English teacher who lives in a California suburb and tells his friends he is writing a memoir about a life-defining summer job he once had at Disneyland.

William Derge, Montgomery Village, MD

William Derge's poems have appeared in *Negative Capability, The Bridge, Artful Dodge, Bellingham Review,* and many other publications. He is the winner of the $1000 2010 Knightsbridge Prize judged by Donald Hall and nominated for a Pushcart Prize. He is a winner of the Rainmaker Award judged by Marge Piercy. He has received honorable mentions in contests sponsored by *The*

Bridge, Sow's Ear, and *New Millennium,* among others. He has been awarded a grant by the Maryland State Arts Council. His work has appeared in several anthologies of Washington poets: *Hungry as We Are* and *Winners.*

Christine Eskilson, Charlestown, MA
Christine Eskilson is an attorney whose writing has received honorable mentions in the 2012 Al Blanchard Short Crime Fiction Contest and the 2012 Women's National Book Association First Annual Writing Contest. Her short stories have appeared in *Blood Moon* and *Rogue Wave,* anthologies of New England crime fiction, and in the *Bethlehem Writers Roundtable.*

Deborah Finklestein, Arlington, MA
Deborah Finkelstein has an MFA in Creative Writing from Goddard College, and is the editor of *Like One,* an anthology that raises money for survivors of the Boston Marathon Bombing. Her poetry has been published in anthologies, newspapers and magazines in nine countries. Recent publications include *Lummox, Ibbetson Street,* and *Cradle Songs*. She also writes plays, and teaches creative writing.

Elaine Ford, Harpswell, ME
Elaine Ford's five novels include *Missed Connections,* set in Somerville, Massachusetts, and *Monkey Bay,* set in rural Maine. Her story collection *The American Wife* won the 2007 Michigan Literary Fiction Award and was published by University of Michigan Press. For her writing Ford has received a Guggenheim fellowship and two National Endowment for the Arts grants. She recently completed *God's Red Clay,* a novel set in 19th-century Alabama and Mississippi. New short fiction appears in *Chariton Review, Iron Horse Literary Review, The Flexible Persona,* and *Arkansas Review*. Ford's website is www.elainefordauthor.com.

E.A. Fow, Brooklyn, NY
E.A. Fow was born and raised in New Zealand but has lived in Brooklyn, New York, for the past twenty years. She holds an MFA in creative writing from Brooklyn College, CUNY and teaches writing and literature at Borough of Manhattan Community College, CUNY. Her academic work concerns inclusive approaches to Joseph Campbell's hero's journey. Fictionwise, her work ranges

from fairy tale and the surreal to literary fiction concerning the post-colonial South Pacific. Her work appears in various print and online anthologies and journals including *Penduline, Sensitive Skin Magazine,* and *Cartography* from Imagination and Place Press.

Alisa A. Gaston-Linn, Loveland, CO

Alisa A. Gaston-Linn's work has appeared in *The Sun, The Montreal Review, Hawaii Pacific Review, Fiction 365, The Faircloth Review, Rocky Mountain Parent, Black Hearts Magazine,* and other publications. She also has an essay in the anthology *Untold Stories: Life, Love and Reproduction* published by Sea Change. Gaston-Linn spent several years as a technical/web writer and editor for the U.S. Antarctic Program and spent three austral summer seasons working in Antarctica. She has taught creative writing to youth at Denver's Lighthouse Writers, and has volunteered as a creative writing facilitator for the Boys & Girls Club, and Urban Peak Teen Shelter. She is currently working on a novel.

Carol L. Gloor, Savanna, IL

A semi-retired attorney, writing for forty years, mostly poetry, her work has appeared in many online and print journals, most recently in the anthology *In Transit,* by Border Town Press, the journal *East on Central,* and in the online journal *Front Porch Review.* She has upcoming work in the online journal *TwoCities Review* and in the print journal *Kerf.* Her poetry chapbook, *Assisted Living,* was published by Finishing Line Press in 2013, and was the winner of the publisher's Starting Gate Award.

Rafael Jesús González, Berkeley, CA

Rafael Jesús González, Professor Emeritus of literature and creative writing, was born in 1935 and raised biculturally/bilingually in El Paso, Texas/Cd. Juárez, Chihuahua. He taught at University of Oregon, Western State Collage of Colorado, Central Washington State University, University of Texas El Paso (visiting Professor of Philosophy), and Laney College, Oakland, California where he founded the Dept. of Mexican & Latin-American Studies. Nominated thrice for a Pushcart Prize, he was honored by the National Council of Teachers of English and Annenberg CPB for his writing in 2003. In 2009 he was honored by the City of Berkeley for his writing, art, teaching, activism for social justice and peace, and received the 2012 Dragonfly Press

Award for Outstanding Literary Achievement. His latest book is *La Musa lunática/The Lunatic Muse* and his work may be read at http://rjgonzalez.blogspot.com.

Meredith Davies Hadaway, Chestertown, MD
Poet and teacher of ecopoetry, Meredith Davies Hadaway is the author of *Fishing Secrets of the Dead, The River is a Reason,* and *At the Narrows* (all from Word Poetry). Her poems have recently appeared in *Salamander, poemmemoirstory,* and *New Ohio Review* and are forthcoming in *Green Writers Press Magazine*. She was the 2013-14 Rose O'Neill Writer-in-Residence at Washington College and a contributor at the inaugural Bread Loaf Orion Environmental Writers Conference.

Pauletta Hansel, Cincinnati, OH
Pauletta Hansel is author of four poetry collections, including *The Lives We Live in Houses* and *What I Did There*. Her fifth, *Tangle,* is forthcoming from Wind Publications. Her work has or will appear in *Atlanta Review, Appalachian Journal, Appalachian Heritage, Now & Then, Kudzu, Talisman, Postcards Poems and Prose, Still: The Journal, Listen Here: Women Writing in Appalachia, The Notebook* and *American Life in Poetry,* among others. She is co-editor of *Pine Mountain Sand & Gravel,* the literary publication of the Southern Appalachian Writers Cooperative. Hansel is a graduate of The Queens University of Charlotte MFA program.

Tom Miller Juvik, Port Orchard, WA
Tom Miller Juvik is a graduate of the University of Washington writing program and began to work with his mentor, novelist Jack Cady. His short fiction has appeared in such publications as *Passager, Glimmer Train, Shadowgraph Magazine,* and *Bryant Literary Review*. He is a recipient of the Hackney Literary Award, Writers' Digest Grand Prize, and the 2014 Stone Canoe Writer's Prize for Veterans. His new novel *The Unspoken Everything* is currently seeking a publisher. In a previous life, he wrote for Comedy Central's *Almost Live* and taught high school social studies. And yes, the neighborhood where he lives happens to have covenants.

Ellen E. Keim, Columbus, OH
Ellen Keim is a Midwestern writer whose work has appeared in online and print magazines, journals, and anthologies. Her

specialties are essays and creative nonfiction about topics as diverse as Islam, the importance of "place," and feminism. She is also the creator of the blog *Femagination* and is working on an historical novel and a memoir.

Jim Landwehr, Waukesha, WI

Jim Landwehr enjoys writing creative non-fiction, fiction, and poetry. His first book, *Dirty Shirt: A Boundary Waters Memoir* was published by eLectio Publishing in June of 2014. His poetry collection, *Written Life,* will be released by eLectio in March of 2015. He has non-fiction stories published in *Neutrons/Protons, Zest Literary Journal, Parody Magazine, Boundary Waters Journal, Forge Journal* and *MidWest Outdoors Magazine*. His poetry has been featured in *Verse Wisconsin, Torrid Literature Journal, Echoes Poetry Journal, Wisconsin People* and *Ideas Magazine,* Off the Coast Poetry Journal, and many others. Landwehr is a Geographic Information Systems Analyst for Waukesha County, his day job, which keeps the lights on and the creditors at bay.

Sandra Sidman Larson, Minnetonka, MN

Sandra's chapbooks *Whistling Girls* and *Cackling Hens* and *Over a Threshold of Roots* were published by Pudding House Publications, and many of her poems have appeared in journals, online sites, anthologies and other venues around the country such as *The Atlanta Review, Gray Sparrow, New Verse News, Earth Daughters, River Poets Journal, Chaminade Literary Review, Jane's Stories II: Anthology of Midwestern Women* (Wild Dove Press), and *What Have You Lost?* (William Morrow & Press). She has been writing poetry since she walked through the doors of The Loft Literary Center of Minneapolis in the mid 1980s.

Dawn Leas, Shavertown, PA

Dawn Leas's work has appeared in *Literary Mama, Southern Women's Review, San Pedro River Review, The Pedestal Magazine* and elsewhere. Her chapbook, *I Know When to Keep Quiet* (Finishing Line Press), is available in print and Kindle versions. A collection of her poems is included in *Everyday Escape Poems* (SwanDive Publishing). She's the associate director of the Wilkes University M.A./M.F.A. Creative Writing programs, and a contributing editor at *Poets' Quarterly, TheThePoetry,* and *CityLitRag*.

Raymond Luczak, Minneapolis, MN
Raymond Luczak is the author and editor of 16 books, the latest titles being *From Heart into Art: Interviews with Deaf and Hard of Hearing Artists and their Allies* and *How to Kill Poetry*. His novel *Men with Their Hands* won first place in the Project: QueerLit Contest 2006. He can be found online at raymondluczak.com.

Mary E. Martin, Rock Hill, SC
Mary E. Martin's poetry has been published in journals such as *Kansas Quarterly, Cimarron Review, Southern Poetry Review, The Main Street Rag*, and most recently, *JAMA, The Journal of the American Medical Association*. Martin's first collection, *The Luminous Disarray*, was published in 1998. She has received three Regional Artist Grants from the Art & Science Council in Charlotte, North Carolina.

Lenard D. Moore, Raleigh, NC
Lenard D. Moore is founder and executive director of the Carolina African American Writers' Collective and writes poetry, essays and reviews. His poems have appeared in more than 100 anthologies, including *Obsession: Sestinas in the Twenty-First Century* (Dartmouth College Press, 2014), *Villanelles* (Knopf, 2012), *The Bedford Introduction to Literature* (Bedford/St. Martin's, 2008) and *The Haiku Anthology* (Norton, 1999). They have also been translated into more than a dozen languages. His most recent book is *A Temple Looming* (WordTech Editions, 2008). He is recipient of the North Carolina Award for Literature (2014), the Raleigh Medal of the Arts for Lifetime Achievement (2008) and Margaret Walker Creative Writing Award (1997), among other awards. He is a Cave Canem Graduate Fellow (1998-2000) and a Soul Mountain Fellow (2007). Moore, an Associate Professor of English, teaches Advanced Poetry Writing and African American Literature at the University of Mount Olive, where he directs the annual literary festival.

Mary Elizabeth Pope, Boston, MA
Mary Elizabeth Pope is Professor of English at Emmanuel College. She is the author of *Divining Venus: Stories* (Waywiser Press, 2013). Her short stories and essays have appeared in literary magazines such as *Florida Review, Bellingham Review, Ascent, Passages North* and others.

Wanda S. Praisner, Bedminster, NJ

Wanda S. Praisner, a recipient of fellowships from the NJ State Council on the Arts, Dodge Foundation, The Provincetown Fine Arts Center, and VCCA, has won the Egan Award, Princemere Prize, Kudzu Competition, and First Prize in Poetry at the College of NJ Writers' Conference. A seven-time Pushcart nominee, she appears in *Atlanta Review, Lullwater Review*, and *Prairie Schooner*. Her latest book is *Sometimes When Something Is Singing* (Antrim House, 2014). She is a resident poet for the state.

Tom Quinn, Warrington, PA

Husband to one and father of two, Tom Quinn has the good fortune of having a long relationship with Main Street Rag Publishing Company with numerous poems appearing in *The Main Street Rag* and short fiction appearing in the *Coming Home* Anthology. A healthcare professional who is lover of great literature and junk food, he spends an inordinate amount of time hiking the Pennsylvania backwoods… wondering.

Renee Ruderman, Denver, CO

Renée Ruderman, an associate professor of English at Metropolitan State University of Denver, Colorado, has two published books, *Poems from the Rooms Below* (Permanence Press, 1995) and *Certain Losses*, a chapbook (Main Street Rag, 2004). She has won prizes for her poems, and some of them have appeared in *The Bellingham Review, I-70 Review, Borderlands*, and the *Raleigh Review*. Ruderman taught at Universität Siegen, Germany, during a sabbatical in 2009, and she recently (2013) taught a poetry workshop at Palacky University in the Czech Republic.

Rikki Santer, Columbus, OH

Rikki Santer teaches literature, writing, and film studies and is an award-winning poet whose work has appeared in numerous publications including *Ms. Magazine, Poetry East, Margie, Asphodel, Alabama Literary Review, Potomac Review, The Adirondack Review, Grimm* and *The Main Street Rag*. Two of her published poetry collections have explored place: *Front Nine* (the Hopewell earthworks of Newark, Ohio) and *Kahiki Redux* (the late Kahiki Supper Club of Columbus, Ohio). *Clothesline Logic*, was published by Pudding House as a finalist in their national chapbook competition, and her latest collection, *Fishing for Rabbits*, was recently published by Kattywompus Press.

Elizabeth Stoessl, Portland, OR

Elizabeth Stoessl lives and writes in Portland, Oregon, after many years on the East Coast and a long career with the Arlington, Virginia, Public Library. Her work has appeared or is forthcoming in numerous journals and anthologies, most recently *Measure, Naugatuck River Review, Persimmon Tree* and *VoiceCatcher*. She was a recipient of a fellowship from the Virginia Center for the Creative Arts.

Bob Strother, Greenville, SC

Award-winning author and two-time Pushcart Prize nominee Bob Strother has had over eighty short stories appear in a number of literary journals and magazines. His collection, *Scattered, Smothered, and Covered,* was released in 2011, and his novel, *Shug's Place* in 2013, both through Main Street Rag Publishing Company. His short story "Doughnut Walk" was adapted for a short film in 2014. Strother is also a contributing author for Southern Writers Magazine.

Brian Behr Valentine, Flat Rock, IL

Brian Behr Valentine, formerly an engineer in the package printing industry, then an international award winning winemaker, is now a consultant in the Midwest. He spends his time verbally fencing with his wife—an improvisational comedienne—wrestling his dogs, and teasing his cats. In addition, he walks across the road to the family farm, has deep talks with his mother, and helps his father split wood, render lard, make sausage, collect maple syrup and skin catfish.

Eric A. Weil, Elizabeth City, NC

Eric A. Weil teaches English at Elizabeth City State University. His poems have won several awards from the North Carolina Poetry Society and have appeared in *Poetry, The Greensboro Review, Dead Mule, Iodine, Silk Road, Wild Goose Poetry Review*, and other journals. Three of his one-act plays have been produced. He also writes quarterly book reviews for *The Main Street Rag.*

Laurelyn Whitt, Minnedosa, Manitoba, Canada
Laurelyn Whitt's poems have appeared in various, primarily North American, journals including *Nimrod International, The Tampa Review, Puerto Del Sol, The Malahat Review, PRISM International, Rattle, Descant* and *The Fiddlehead*. The author of four award-winning poetry collections, her most recent book, *Tether* (Seraphim Editions: Woodstock, Ontario) won the 2013 Lansdowne Prize for Poetry. She lives in Minnedosa, Manitoba.

E.G. Willy, Walnut Creek, CA
Willy is a West Coast writer. His stories have appeared in journals, anthologies, and magazines in the U.S., Great Britain, and Canada. His spoken word pieces have aired on public and college radio shows around the country. He writes principally in English but has been known to publish pieces in Spanish when he is taken by the spirit of a misspent youth.

About the Editor:

Alice Osborn, Raleigh, NC
Alice Osborn's past educational and work experience is unusually varied, and it now feeds her work as a poet (*After the Steaming Stops* and *Unfinished Projects* are both from Main Street Rag Publishing Company), as well as an editor-for-hire and popular writing coach. In the past decade, Osborn has taught classes and writing workshops to thousands of aspiring authors of nearly all ages from 9 to 90 both around the block and internationally. Along with this anthology which feeds her lifelong fascination with houses, Alice is the editor of *Tattoos*, from Main Street Rag Publishing Company. A North Carolina Writers' Network board member and a Pushcart Prize nominee, her work has appeared in the *News and Observer, The Broad River Review, The Pedestal Magazine, Soundings Review* and in numerous journals and anthologies. When she's not editing or writing, Alice is a competitive Irish dancer, and plays guitar and violin. She lives in Raleigh, North Carolina, with her husband, two children and four very messy and loud birds. Visit her website at www.aliceosborn.com.